Floating and Sinking

TEACHER'S GUIDE

SCIENCE AND TECHNOLOGY FOR CHILDREN®

NATIONAL SCIENCE RESOURCES CENTER
Smithsonian Institution • National Academy of Sciences
Arts and Industries Building, Room 1201
Washington, DC 20560

NSRC

The National Science Resources Center is operated by the Smithsonian Institution and the National Academy of Sciences to improve the teaching of science in the nation's schools. The NSRC collects and disseminates information about exemplary teaching resources, develops and disseminates curriculum materials, and sponsors outreach activities, specifically in the areas of leadership development and technical assistance, to help school districts develop and sustain hands-on science programs.

STC Project Supporters

National Science Foundation
Smithsonian Institution
U.S. Department of Defense
U.S. Department of Education
John D. and Catherine T. MacArthur Foundation
The Dow Chemical Company Foundation
E. I. du Pont de Nemours & Company
Amoco Foundation, Inc.
Hewlett-Packard Company
Smithsonian Institution Educational Outreach Fund
Smithsonian Women's Committee

This project was supported, in part,
by the
National Science Foundation
Opinions expressed are those of the authors
and not necessarily those of the Foundation

ISBN 0-89278-940-9

Published by Carolina Biological Supply Company, 2700 York Road, Burlington, NC 27215.
Call toll free 1-800-334-5551.

This material is based upon work supported by the National Science Foundation under Grant No. ESI-9252947. Any opinions, findings, and conclusions or recommendations expressed in this material are those of the author(s) and do not necessarily reflect the views of the National Science Foundation.

CB787200109
♻ Printed on recycled paper.

Foreword

Since 1988, the National Science Resources Center (NSRC) has been developing Science and Technology for Children® (STC®), an innovative hands-on science program for children in grades kindergarten through six. The 24 units of the STC program, four for each grade level, are designed to provide all students with stimulating experiences in the life, earth, and physical sciences and technology while simultaneously developing their critical-thinking and problem-solving skills.

The STC units provide children with the opportunity to learn age-appropriate concepts and skills and to acquire scientific attitudes and habits of mind. In the primary grades, children begin their study of science by observing, measuring, and identifying properties. Then they move on through a progression of experiences that culminate in grade six with the design of controlled experiments.

The "Focus-Explore-Reflect-Apply" learning cycle incorporated into the STC units is based on

Alignment of STC® and STC/MS™ Science Curriculum Modules

Grade Level		Life and Earth Sciences		Physical Science and Technology	
STC	K–1	Organisms	Weather	Solids and Liquids	Comparing and Measuring
	2	The Life Cycle of Butterflies	Soils	Changes	Balancing and Weighing
	3	Plant Growth and Development	Rocks and Minerals	Chemical Tests	Sound
	4	Animal Studies	Land and Water	Electric Circuits	Motion and Design
	5	Microworlds	Ecosystems	Food Chemistry	Floating and Sinking
	6	Experiments with Plants	Measuring Time	Magnets and Motors	The Technology of Paper
STC/MS	6–8	Human Body Systems	Catastrophic Events	Properties of Matter	Energy, Machines, and Motion
	6–8	Organisms—From Macro to Micro	Earth in Space	Light	Electrical Energy and Circuit Design

Note: All STC units can be used at one grade level above or below the level indicated on the chart. STC/MS units can also be used at grade 9.

Sequence of Development of Scientific Reasoning Skills

Scientific Reasoning Skills	Grades					
	1	2	3	4	5	6
Observing, Measuring, and Identifying Properties	♦	♦	♦	♦	♦	♦
Seeking Evidence Recognizing Patterns and Cycles		♦	♦	♦	♦	♦
Identifying Cause and Effect Extending the Senses				♦	♦	♦
Designing and Conducting Controlled Experiments						♦

research findings about children's learning. These findings indicate that knowledge is actively constructed by each learner and that children learn science best in a hands-on experimental environment where they can make their own discoveries. The steps of the learning cycle are as follows:

- Focus: Explore and clarify the ideas that children already have about the topic.

- Explore: Enable children to engage in hands-on explorations of the objects, organisms, and science phenomena to be investigated.

- Reflect: Encourage children to discuss their observations and to reconcile their ideas.

- Apply: Help children discuss and apply their new ideas in new situations.

The learning cycle in STC units gives students opportunities to develop increased understanding of important scientific concepts and to develop positive attitudes toward science.

The STC units provide teachers with a variety of strategies with which to assess student learning. The STC units also offer teachers opportunities to link the teaching of science with the development of skills in mathematics, language arts, and social studies. In addition, the STC units encourage the use of cooperative learning to help students develop the valuable skill of working together.

In the extensive research and development process used with all STC units, scientists and educators, including experienced elementary school teachers, act as consultants to teacher-developers, who research, trial teach, and write the units. The process begins with the developer researching the unit's content and pedagogy. Then, before writing the unit, the developer trial teaches lessons in public school classrooms in the metropolitan Washington, D.C., area. Once a unit is written, the NSRC evaluates its effectiveness with children by field-testing it nationally in ethnically diverse urban, rural, and suburban public schools. At the field-testing stage, the assessment sections in each unit are also evaluated by the Program Evaluation and Research Group of Lesley College, located in Cambridge, Mass. The final editions of the units reflect the incorporation of teacher and student field-test feedback and of comments on accuracy and soundness from the leading scientists and science educators who serve on the STC Advisory Panel.

The STC project would not have been possible without the generous support of numerous federal agencies, private foundations, and corporations. Supporters include the National Science Foundation, the Smithsonian Institution, the U.S. Department of Defense, the U.S. Department of Education, the John D. and Catherine T. MacArthur Foundation, the Dow Chemical Company Foundation, the Amoco Foundation, Inc., E. I. du Pont de Nemours & Company, the Hewlett-Packard Company, the Smithsonian Institution Educational Outreach Fund, and the Smithsonian Women's Committee.

Acknowledgments

Floating and Sinking was developed and drafted by David Hartney, and the final edition was written by David Hartney in collaboration with the STC development and production team. The unit was edited by Marilyn Fenichel and illustrated by Martha Vaughan, Max-Karl Winkler, Catherine Corder, and Heidi M. Kupke. It was trial taught in the Margaret Amidon Elementary School in Washington, DC. Several activities were adapted from *Sink or Float,* a unit developed by the Elementary Science Study at the Education Development Center in 1971.

The technical review of *Floating and Sinking* was conducted by:

Jack Easley, Professor of Physics, University of Illinois at Urbana-Champagne, Urbana, IL

John Layman, Professor of Physics and Education, University of Maryland, College Park, MD

Ramon E. Lopez, Department of Astronomy, University of Maryland, College Park, MD

The NSRC would like to thank the following individuals and school systems for their assistance with the national field-testing of the unit:

Iowa City Public Schools, Iowa City, IA
Coordinator: Jeanne Jones, Staff Developer for Elementary Science
Julie Piper, Teacher, Coralville Central Elementary School
Mary Thunhorst, Teacher, Twain Elementary School
Pat Zioborek, Teacher, Lucas Elementary School

Los Angeles Unified School District, Los Angeles, CA
Coordinator: Cheuk Choi, Teacher Adviser, Region B
Luella Derry, Teacher, San Pascual Avenue School
Cheryl Hildreth, Teacher, Twenty-Fourth Street School
Connie Wright, Teacher, Multnomah Street School

School District of University City, University City, MO
Coordinator: Clara McCrary, Science Coordinator
James Klevorn, Teacher, Flynn Park School
D'Anne Shelton, Teacher, Delmar-Harvard School
Jack Wiegers, Consultant, Project SEER (Science Education for Equity Reform)
Katina Willis, Teacher, Daniel Boone School

Traverse City Area Public Schools, Traverse City, MI
Coordinator: Linda Williams, K-12 Science Coordinator
Gerri Milarch, Teacher, Oak Park Elementary School

Jim Smith, Teacher, Norris Elementary School
Claire Stephenson, Teacher, Glenn Loomis Elementary School

The NSRC also would like to thank the following individuals for their contributions to the unit:

David Babcock, Director, Board of Cooperative Educational Services, Second Supervisory District, Monroe-Orleans Counties, Spencerport, NY

Judi Backman, Math/Science Coordinator, Highline Public Schools, Seattle, WA

L. J. Benton, Coordinator, Instructional Materials Processing Center, Fairfax County Public Schools, Fairfax, VA

Brenda Collum, Science Coordinator, Margaret Amidon Elementary School, Washington, DC

Debby Deal, Educational Consultant, Clifton, VA

JoAnn E. DeMaria, Teacher, Hutchison Elementary School, Herndon, VA

Kathleen Fay, Bailey's Elementary School for the Arts and Sciences, Fairfax, VA

Joe Griffith, Director, Hands-on Science Program, National Museum of American History, Smithsonian Institution, Washington, DC

Pauline Hamlette, Principal, Margaret Amidon Elementary School Washington, DC

Charles Hardy, Assistant Superintendent, Instruction and Curriculum, Highline Public Schools, Seattle, WA

Paul Johnston, Curator, Division of Transportation, National Museum of American History, Smithsonian Institution, Washington, DC

Jack Kalina, Researcher, Division of Transportation, National Museum of American History, Smithsonian Institution, Washington, DC

Barbara Kelley, Teacher, Margaret Amidon Elementary School, Washington, DC

Herb Lin, Staff Officer, Computer Science and Telecommunication Board, National Academy of Sciences, Washington, DC

Robert Lowry, Researcher, Division of Transportation, National Museum of American History, Smithsonian Institution, Washington, DC

Diana Martin, Teacher, Bailey's Elementary School for the Arts and Sciences, Fairfax, VA

Mary Ellen McCaffrey, Photographic Production Control, Smithsonian Institution, Washington, DC

Patricia McGlashan, Educational Consultant, Stony Creek, CT

Richard McQueen, Teacher/Learning Manager, Alpha High School, Gresham, OR

Dane Penland, Chief, Imaging and Technology Services Branch, Office of Printing and Photographic Services, Smithsonian Institution, Washington, DC

Laura Pierce, STC Assistant (1990-92), Fairfax, VA

Richard Philbrick, Researcher, Division of Transportation, National Museum of American History, Smithsonian Institution, Washington, DC

Charles Rauson, Researcher, Division of Transportation, National Museum of American History, Smithsonian Institution, Washington, DC

Susan Sprague, Director of Science and Social Studies, Mesa Public Schools, Mesa, AZ

Richard W. Strauss, Photographer, Office of Printing and Photographic Services, Smithsonian Institution, Washington, DC

Rick Vargas, Photographer, Office of Printing and Photographic Services, Smithsonian Institution, Washington, DC

The librarians and staff of the Central Reference Service, Smithsonian Institution Libraries, Washington, DC

The NSRC is indebted to all of the above individuals, who were instrumental in ensuring the scientific accuracy and pedagogical usefulness of the learning activities in this unit.

Sally Goetz Shuler
Executive Director
National Science Resources Center

STC Advisory Panel

Science Notebooks in the STC Classroom

Writing is one of the ways that children learn in science. . . . When children explain what they have seen and why they think this occurs in writing, they are forced to clarify their thoughts and organize these ideas in a way that others can understand.

Jenny Feely
"Writing in Science"
in *Science & Language Links*

Every student in an STC classroom should be required to keep a science notebook. Students in grades 3 through 6 can use a loose-leaf binder or a composition book for this purpose; first- and second-graders write directly in their consumable STC Student Notebooks. Students should keep their notebooks with them throughout science class, so that they can add entries daily and review their notes as the unit progresses. Teachers are encouraged to review students' notebook entries periodically to assess their progress in recording the results of their investigations and the growth in their understanding of important concepts.

Why Is a Science Notebook Important?

Science notebooks are important for many reasons. The first reason is that writing is an integral part of the process of learning science. By using notebooks, students model one of the most vital and enduring functions of scientists in all disciplines—recording data. Scientists across the world record their observations and conclusions, as well as comments on their readings and reflections. They rely on their notes when sharing their findings with peers and when preparing the papers in which they share their work with the broader scientific community. The notebooks of famous scientists such as Galileo and Albert Einstein have become part of the world's cultural heritage.

A second reason for maintaining a science notebook is that it provides the student with a ready reference during the unit as well as a resource to consult when reviewing materials at the end of the unit. The notebook is also a means of communicating with other students and with the teacher.

A science notebook encourages the students' creativity. Students are encouraged to draw as well as to write in their notebooks. Keeping a notebook also enhances students' writing skills. It gives them practice in organizing materials and in expressing themselves clearly. At the same time, notebook writing can encourage students to connect science with other areas of the curriculum. Extensions in the STC units, for example, ask students to write poems, stories, or songs, or to do research in related areas such as history and geography.

Another advantage of notebooks is that they get students more involved in science. Students take ownership of their notebooks. As the unit progresses, they have a growing sense of pride in what they have written and learned. Their confidence in their science learning, as well as in their overall knowledge and skills, grows.

Finally, the science notebook offers the teacher a unique means of assessing student progress in science learning. The notebook, ideally begun during the first lesson of the unit and continued to its conclusion, is a tool that can be used to assess the growth in students' understanding of science as well as in their ability to summarize and capture their findings.

Science notebooks are tools for inquiry that allow children to frame questions and seek answers. . . . They are to be used to identify student understanding and misconceptions about science concepts and to inform further practice.

Science Notebook Guidebook
Cambridge Public Schools
Cambridge, Mass.

Incorporating Science Notebooks Into Classroom Activity

Making time for students to write in their notebooks daily can be challenging. With proper planning, however, writing becomes a natural part of the rhythm of the science class.

When to Write
The time at which writing is done depends on the nature of the classroom activity on a given day and on the teacher's choice. What is most important is that students have sufficient time to write, and that they have an opportunity to write in their notebooks daily.

During some inquiries, things may go more smoothly if students suspend their hands-on investigations at certain points, write in their notebooks, and then resume their activity. In other cases, the best time to write is after the inquiry ends. Teachers should allow time for students to share their writing with their peers and the entire class.

Even though students have used their notebooks repeatedly during a lesson, time should always be left at the end of a lesson for students to reflect on what they have learned and to write down any new questions that have arisen.

Notebook Materials
Student notebook materials are diverse. Students may use a bound composition book or a loose-leaf notebook; they can even staple sheets of construction paper around blank or lined paper. Many teachers prefer loose-leaf notebooks because they are more flexible. Folders with pockets and fasteners for three-hole paper also work well because they provide storage space for record sheets, graph paper, and other materials. Other teachers prefer composition books, which deter students from removing or deleting past recordings. Students can glue or tape their record sheets into the composition books.

Notebook Organization
Teachers should make sure that all the students in the class organize their notebooks in the same way. The notebooks should, for example, begin with a table of contents. Students can allow several pages for this at the beginning of the unit. As they begin each lesson, students can then add the title of the lesson to their table of contents. Students should always date their entries and number the pages consecutively throughout the unit. Tabs can help students organize their notebooks and locate specific sections more easily.

Getting Started
Students who have not used science notebooks may need some initial guidance on how to use them most effectively.

You might want to begin by facilitating a brainstorming session designed to increase students' awareness of the importance of maintaining a notebook. Then present some guidelines such as those noted in the previous section.

Tell students that you will be looking at the notebooks often to see how they are doing. At the same time, emphasize that the notebook is primarily for their own benefit. Stress that they should write down not only facts and observations but also questions and ideas they want to further explore.

Help them understand that they should use their notebooks in two major ways. First, they should "take notes" on what they have seen, experienced, and concluded. As they move through the investigation, students should also "make notes"—that is, ask questions and pose comments. Emphasize the importance of always writing clearly and of expressing thoughts in an organized way.

Urge students to use drawings as well as text. They should also be encouraged to design tables and graphs to display findings.

Explain that when you look at the notebooks, you will consider many things. You will look at how complete their entries are. You will also try to determine how much effort they have put into their answers and questions. For a science notebook, this is more important than the "right" answers. Students should think of the information in their notebooks as a rough draft; therefore, you will not assess them on the basis of style, correct spelling, or word usage. The notebooks should, however, be neat and clearly written. The notes that scientists keep must be readable by other scientists, and students' notebooks should meet this same standard.

Organizing the Notebooks
When talking about a good way to organize the notebooks, you might also tell students that the information they write down should be a record of the basic components of their scientific inquiry. These steps are as follows:

- The question that the student wants to answer

- A prediction about how the inquiry will turn out

- The student's plan for the inquiry and the materials that he or she will use

- The student's data and observations (includes words, tables and graphs, and illustrations)

- The student's conclusions
- Next steps or new questions that have arisen from the inquiry

STC lessons generally end with a discussion, during which students share their findings and suggest additional questions to explore. When the discussion ends, you may ask students to return to their notebooks and to summarize, in their own words, the major ideas that have emerged during this discussion. Have students separate these final comments from their previous notes by a horizontal line, which is called the "line of learning."

Keeping a Science Notebook: Student Objectives

After sufficient practice, students who keep science notebooks should be able to do the following:

- Increase their understanding of science concepts.

- Use writing as a process for discovery.

- Improve their ability to organize ideas and information.

- Recognize the connection between thinking and writing.

- Write more freely, more comfortably, and more often.

Adapted from
"Writing for Understanding"
in *Science and Writing Connections*

Reviewing Science Notebooks

Check the students' science notebooks often. Glance at the notebooks during class and collect them periodically for a more detailed review.

You may give feedback to students in many ways. Some teachers prefer to use Post-it Notes™; others write on the notebook page itself; others may prefer to enter their comments in the back of the book. Use a color that is distinguishable from the black or blue that students generally use (green is one idea); it's best not to use red ink. Some teachers ask students to bring their tape recorders to school so they make their comments into the recorder.

Make your feedback positive and constructive. Grade students for the completeness of their work and for their effort. Do not grade ideas as

"right" or "wrong." Misspellings or grammatical errors should not be circled or criticized in the notebook. Date and initial all your written comments.

To bring objectivity to the assessment process, some teachers use rubrics. A simple assessment rubric is as follows:

Rubric for Assessing Science Notebooks

STANDARD	SCORE
Date and purpose of inquiry	
Appropriate prediction	
List of materials	
Sequence of procedures	
Diagrams and labels	
Chart or data table as it corresponds to student's results	
Conclusions as they relate to data and answers to the inquiry questions	

3 = Achieved the standard with honors.
2 = Achieved the standard.
1 = Achievement below the standard.
0 = No evidence of achievement.

Conclusion

Student notebooks fill many roles. They promote students' science learning and give students an opportunity to enhance their writing skills. They help students better appreciate the process of scientific inquiry. They help students organize their learning and, by the end of the unit, realize how much they have learned. For teachers, notebooks are a unique means of reviewing student learning.

These guidelines should help you and your students take full advantage of the many benefits that student science notebooks bring to the STC classroom.

Acknowledgment

The NSRC thanks the Cambridge Public Schools and Beckman@Science for providing materials on writing and assessing student science notebooks.

References

Reading
Baker, L., Dreher, M.J., and Guthrie, J. *Engaging Young Readers*. New York: Guilford Publications, Inc. 2000.

Gaskins, I., Guthrie, J., et al. Integrating instruction of science, reading, and writing: Goals, teacher development, and assessment. *Journal of Research in Science Teaching*, 31, 1039-1056. 1994.

Guthrie, J. Educational contexts for engagement in literacy. *The Reading Teacher*, 49, 432-445. 1996.

Guthrie, J., Anderson, E., Alao, S., and Rinehart, J. Influences of concept-oriented reading instruction on strategy use and conceptual learning from text. *The Elementary School Journal*, 99, 343-366. 1999.

Guthrie, J., Cox, K., et al. Principles of integrated instruction for engagement in reading. *Educational Psychology Review*, 10, 177-199. 1998.

Guthrie, J. T., Van Meter, P., Hancock, G.R., et al. Does concept-oriented reading instruction increase strategy use and conceptual learning from text? *Journal of Educational Psychology*, 90, 261-278. 1998.

Palinscar, A.S., and Brown, A.L. Reciprocal teaching of comprehension-fostering and comprehension-monitoring activities. *Cognition and Instruction*, 1(2), 117-175. 1984.

Romance, N., and Vitale, M. A curriculum strategy that expands time for in-depth elementary science instruction by using science-based reading strategies: Effects of a year-long study in grade four. *Journal of Research in Science Teaching*, 29, 545-554. 1992.

Science Notebook Writing

Baxter, G., Bass, K., and Glaser, R. Notebook writing in three fifth-grade science classrooms. *The Elementary School Journal*. 2001.

Beckman@Science. *Introduction to Science Notebooks*. Irvine, Calif.

Cambridge Science Department, Cambridge Public Schools. *Science Notebook Guidebook*. Cambridge, Mass. 2001.

Feely, Jenny. Writing in science. In: Scott, J. *Science & Language Links: Classroom Implications*. Portsmouth, N.H.: Heinemann. 1993.

Freedman, R.L.H. *Science and Writing Connections*. Palo Alto, Calif.: Dale Seymour Publications. 1999.

Keys, C.W. Revitalizing instruction in the scientific genres: Connecting knowledge production with writing to learn in science. *Science Education*, 83, 115-130. 1999.

Klentschy, M., Garrison, L., and Amaral, O.M. (1999). Valle Imperial Project in Science (VIPS) Four-Year Comparison of Student Achievement Data 1995–1999. El Centro, Calif. 1999.

National Council of Teachers of English and The International Reading Association. *Standards for the English Language Arts.* Urbana, Ill.: NCTE. 1996.

Shepardson, D.P., and Britsch, S.J. Children's science journals: Tools for teaching, learning, and assessing. *Science and Children*, 34, 13-7; 46-47. 1997.

Reif, R.J., and Rauch, K. Science in their own words. *Science and Children*, 31, 31-33. 1994.

Daniels, H. *Literature Circles, Voice and Choice in the Student-Centered Classroom*. York, Maine: Stenhouse Publishers. 1994.

Contents

Goals for *Floating and Sinking*

In this unit, students investigate the phenomenon of buoyancy. From their experiences, they are introduced to the following concepts, skills, and attitudes.

Concepts

- Several variables affect the buoyancy of an object.

- Water pushes up on both floating and submerged objects with a buoyant force; objects push down on the water.

- The buoyant force on large objects is greater than the buoyant force on smaller objects.

- The amount of water an object displaces is directly related to the object's volume.

- Because of buoyant force, objects appear to weigh less when they are submerged.

- Objects that weigh more than the same volume of water sink; objects that weigh less than the same volume of water float.

- Salt water weighs more than an equal amount of fresh water.

- The buoyancy of an object varies with the density of the liquid.

Skills

- Observing, recording, and organizing test results.

- Applying previous experiences to make predictions.

- Creating and analyzing graphs.

- Calibrating a spring scale and using it to measure the magnitude of a force.

- Reading science materials for information.

- Communicating results through writing and discussion.

- Solving a problem that requires the application of previously learned concepts and skills.

Attitudes

- Developing an interest in investigating floating, sinking, and related phenomena.

- Recognizing the importance of repeating a test or measurement and comparing results.

Unit Overview and Materials List

Children of all ages are curious about why some objects float while others sink. They have probably had a number of experiences playing in water with a variety of objects. They may also have seen air bubbles rising through the water after someone jumps in, or watched boats, leaves, or sticks floating in a pond. Some may have noticed that they sink in the bathtub but float in the ocean.

From such observations and experiences, children have developed ideas and questions about floating and sinking. They may think that weight has something to do with why things sink or float. Others may suspect that size or even the liquid plays a role. How these factors and others affect the behavior of objects in liquids is the focus of *Floating and Sinking*, a 16-lesson unit for fifth-graders. The activities in this unit provide experiences upon which children can build a more complete understanding of the phenomenon of buoyancy.

Lesson 1 begins with a pre-unit assessment of students' ideas and questions about floating and sinking. In Lessons 2 through 5, they begin to test their ideas, focusing first on weight and size. In addition, they investigate and calibrate a device for weighing objects—a spring scale. Students make predictions and then test them with experiments. They record observations, discuss their ideas with classmates, measure the weight of a variety of objects, and begin a class graph of their observations. By the end of Lesson 5, students will have made surprising discoveries: some "floaters" are heavier than some "sinkers," and the largest objects are not always the heaviest.

In Lessons 6, 7, and 8, students test variables by constructing and testing boats of various shapes, sizes, and materials. Students make clay boats and explore how weight can be distributed to make a sinker into a floater. They then load them with marbles to see how much cargo different-sized boats will keep afloat. These activities give students information about the relationship between the variables of size, weight, and design.

In Lessons 9 through 12, students focus on the behavior of objects when they are submerged in water. First, they use the spring scale to measure the buoyant force on different-sized fishing bobbers. Then they measure the change in water level caused by objects submerged in a graduated tube.

When students measure the weight of a variety of submerged objects, they discover that because of the buoyant force, objects appear to weigh less when they are submerged. Holding size and volume constant, students weigh water and compare its weight with that of solid objects. This experience provides an interesting observation: objects that weigh more than the same volume of water sink, while objects that weigh less than the same volume of water float.

In Lessons 13, 14, and 15, students investigate the behavior of objects in salt water. They dissolve salt in water and compare the weight of the water with the weight of the salt water. Then they test the objects they have worked with previously to see if they float or sink in salt water. Here, students discover that because salt water is heavier than fresh water, some objects (the acrylic cylinders and the nylon bolt) that sank in fresh water can float in salt water. In Lesson 15, students construct a scientific instrument called a hydrometer and compare the level at which it floats in graduated cylinders of fresh and salt water. Through this activity, students expand their understanding of buoyant force and displacement.

Lesson 16 provides an excellent opportunity to assess student learning. Students are challenged to apply what they have learned from their previous experiences with buoyancy. They make and test predictions about an unknown "mystery cylinder."

In *Floating and Sinking*, students become engrossed in the activities and generate many questions about what they observe. To assist you in helping students find out answers for themselves, the unit provides background information, diagrams, extensions, and reading selections. Assessments that are embedded in many lessons give you information for evaluating students' learning. Matched pre- and post-unit assessments enable you to document growth in students' concepts of buoyancy. Additional assessments are also included in the unit, as well as a bibliography of other resources related to this topic.

Materials List

Below is a list of materials needed for the *Floating and Sinking* unit. Please note that the metric and English equivalent measurements in this unit are approximate.

1	Teacher's Guide
15	Student Activity Books
30	resealable plastic bags
15	plastic tubes, 4.5 × 16 cm (1¾ × 6″)
2	boxes of kosher salt, 1.42 kg (3 lb)
2	acrylic beads
15	plastic teaspoons
15	plastic tanks, 4 liters (1 gal)
15	plastic plates
6	sponges
6	plastic buckets with handles, 4 liters (1 gal) capacity each
15	sets of objects: large and small cylinders made of aluminum, acrylic (clear plastic), wood, and polyethylene; a fishing bobber; a nylon bolt; an aluminum nut; a ball of clay; a marble; and a wood bead
15	spring scales
2	rolls of ½″ masking tape
15	large bobby pins
15	small resealable bags
5	boxes of jumbo paper clips
*2	boxes of No. 1 paper clips
4	packages of oil-based modeling clay, 500 g (1 lb) each
2	equal-arm balances
450	glass marbles
1	roll of heavy duty aluminum foil
15	fishing bobbers, 32 mm (1¼″)
15	fishing bobbers, 38 mm (1½″)
15	fishing bobbers, 45 mm (1¾″)
1	roll of braided casting line, 12 m (39 ft)

15	pieces of cardboard, 8 cm (3″) square
15	small suction cups with metal hook
15	plastic cylindrical containers, 2.5 × 2.5 cm (1 × 1″)
1	box of flat, wooden toothpicks
30	small plastic tasting spoons
15	plastic droppers
30	plastic cups and lids, 300 ml (10 oz)
30	small plastic drinking straws
1	permanent marker
15	black acetyl delrin cylinders, 2.5 × 2.5 cm (1 × 1″)
15	black acetyl delrin cylinders, 1.25 × 1.25 cm (½ × ½″)
1	roll of waxed paper
1	pack of towels
**30	science notebooks
**	Newsprint
**	Pencils
**	Water
**	Bulletin board
**	Thumb tacks
**	Rulers

*Note: The smaller No. 1 paper clips are used in creating the class graph.

**Note: These items are not included in the kit. They are available in most schools or can be brought from home.

Teaching *Floating and Sinking*

The following information on unit structure, teaching strategies, materials, and assessment will help you give students the guidance they need to make the most of their hands-on experiences with this unit.

Unit Structure

How Lessons Are Organized in the Teacher's Guide: Each lesson in the *Floating and Sinking* Teacher's Guide provides you with a brief overview, lesson objectives, key background information, materials list, advance preparation instructions, step-by-step procedures, and helpful management tips. Many of the lessons include recommended guidelines for assessment. Lessons also frequently indicate opportunities for curriculum integration. Look for the following icons that highlight extension ideas:

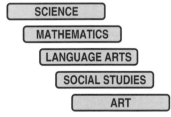

Please note that all record sheets, blackline masters, student instructions, and reading selections may be copied and used in conjunction with the teaching of this unit. For purposes of classroom use only, you may make an overhead transparency of a specific page or item in the Teacher's Guide or Student Activity Book.

Student Activity Book: The *Floating and Sinking* Student Activity Book accompanies the Teacher's Guide. Written specifically for students, this activity book contains simple instructions and illustrations to help students understand how to conduct the activities in this unit. The Student Activity Book also will help students follow along with you as you guide each lesson, and it will provide guidance for students who may miss a lesson (or who do not immediately grasp certain activities or concepts). In addition to previewing each lesson in the Teacher's Guide, you may find it helpful to preview the accompanying lesson in the Student Activity Book.

The lessons in the Student Activity Book are divided into the following sections, paralleling the Teacher's Guide:

- **Think and Wonder** sketches for students a general picture of the ideas and activities of the lesson described in the **Overview and Objectives** of the Teacher's Guide

- **Materials** lists the materials students and their partners or teammates will be using

- **Find Out for Yourself** flows in tandem with the steps in the **Procedure** section of the Teacher's Guide and briefly and simply walks students through the lesson's activities

- **Ideas to Explore,** which frequently echoes the **Extensions** section in the Teacher's Guide, gives students additional activities to try out or ideas to think about

Teaching Strategies

Classroom Discussion: Class discussions, effectively led by the teacher, are important vehicles for science learning. Research shows that the way questions are asked, as well as the time allowed for responses, can contribute to the quality of the discussion.

When you ask questions, think about what you want to achieve in the ensuing discussion. For example, open-ended questions, for which there is no one right answer, will encourage students to give creative and thoughtful answers. You can use other types of questions to encourage students to see specific relationships and contrasts or to help them summarize and draw conclusions. It is good practice to mix these questions. It also is good practice always to give students "wait time" before expecting them to answer; this will encourage broader participation and more thoughtful answers. You will want to monitor responses, looking for additional situations that invite students to formulate hypotheses, make generalizations, and explain how they arrived at a conclusion.

Brainstorming: Brainstorming is a whole-class exercise in which students contribute their thoughts about a particular idea or problem. When used to introduce a new science topic, it can be a stimulating and productive exercise. It also is a useful and efficient way for the teacher to find out what students know and think about a topic. As students learn the rules for brainstorming, they will become more and more adept in their participation.

To begin a brainstorming session, define for students the topics about which they will share ideas. Explain the following rules to students:

■ Accept all ideas without judgment.

■ Do not criticize or make unnecessary comments about the contributions of others.

■ Try to connect your ideas to the ideas of others.

Cooperative Learning Groups: One of the best ways to teach hands-on science is to arrange students in small groups. Materials and procedures for *Floating and Sinking* are based on groups of two. There are several advantages to this organization. It provides a small forum for students to express their ideas and get feedback. It also offers pupils a chance to learn from each other by sharing ideas, discoveries, and skills. With coaching, students can develop important interpersonal skills that will serve them well in all aspects of life. As students work, they will often find it productive to talk about what they are doing, resulting in a steady hum of conversation. If you or others in the school are accustomed to a quiet room, this new, busy atmosphere may require some adjustment.

Learning Centers: You can give supplemental science materials a permanent home in the classroom in a spot designated as the learning center. Students can use the center in a number of ways: as an "on your own" project center, as an observation post, as a trade-book reading nook, or simply as a place to spend unscheduled time when assignments are done. To keep interest in the center high, change the learning center or add to it often. Here are a few suggestions of items to include:

■ Science trade books on ships and shipwrecks, water, life under water, and buoyancy (see **Appendix B: Bibliography** for suggested titles)

■ Audiovisual materials on related subjects, such as the ocean, boats and ships, and submarines

■ Items contributed by students for sharing, such as magazine or newspaper articles, pictures, maps, and models

Materials

Safety Notes: This unit does not contain anything of a highly toxic nature, but common sense dictates that nothing be put in the mouth. In fact, it is good practice to tell your students that, in science, materials are never tasted. Students may also need to be reminded that certain items, such as dropper bottles, toothpicks, and straws, should be used only as directed.

Organization of Materials: To help ensure an orderly progression through the unit, you will need to establish a system for storing and distributing materials. Being prepared is the key to success. Here are a few suggestions:

■ Read through the **Materials List** on pg. 4. Begin to collect the items you will need that are not provided in the kit.

■ Know which activity is scheduled and which materials will be used.

■ Familiarize yourself with the materials as soon as possible.

■ Organize your students so that they are involved in distributing and returning materials. If you have an existing network of cooperative groups, delegate the responsibility to one member of each group.

■ Organize a distribution center and instruct your students to pick up and return supplies to that area. A cafeteria-style approach works especially well when there are large numbers of items to distribute.

■ Many activities in this unit involve distributing and collecting water. You will need to establish an effective method for handling water in your classroom. Other classrooms have found buckets with handles to be a good way to distribute and pour water. Sponges and plastic plates can be used to contain and clean up spills.

- Look at each lesson ahead of time. Some have specific suggestions for handling materials needed that day.

- Minimize cleanup by providing each working group with a cleanup box and a packet of paper towels. Students can put disposable materials into this box and clean off their tables at the end of each lesson.

- Management tips are provided throughout the unit. Look for the icon at the right.

Assessment

Philosophy: In the Science and Technology for Children program, assessment is an ongoing, integral part of instruction. Because assessment emerges naturally from the activities in the lessons, students are assessed in the same manner in which they are taught. They may, for example, perform experiments, record their observations, or make oral presentations. Such assessments permit the examination of processes as well as of products, emphasizing what students know and can do.

The learning goals in STC units include a number of different science concepts, skills, and attitudes. Therefore, a number of different strategies are provided to help you assess and document your students' progress toward the goals (see Figure T-2). These strategies also will help you report to parents and appraise your own teaching. In addition, the assessments will enable your students to view their own progress, reflect on their learning, and formulate further questions for investigation and research.

Figure T-2 summarizes the goals and assessment strategies for this unit. The left-hand column lists the individual goals for the unit and the lessons in which they are addressed. The right-hand column identifies lessons containing assessment sections to which you can turn for specific assessment strategies. These strategies are summarized as bulleted items.

Assessment Strategies: The assessment strategies in STC units fall into three categories: matched pre- and post-unit assessments, embedded assessments, and additional assessments.

The first lesson of each STC unit is a *pre-unit assessment* designed to give you information

Figure T-1

Sample of matched pre- and post-unit class discussions

about what the whole class and individual students already know about the unit's topic and what they want to find out. It often includes a brainstorming session during which students share their thoughts about the topic through exploring one or two basic questions. In the *post-unit assessment* following the final lesson, the class revisits the pre-unit assessment questions, giving you two sets of comparable data that indicate students' growth in knowledge and skills (see Figure T-1).

Throughout a unit, assessments are woven into, or embedded in, lessons. These *embedded*

continued on pg. 10

Floating and Sinking: Goals and Assessment Strategies

Concepts	
Goals	**Assessment Strategies**
Several variables affect the buoyancy of an object. Lessons 1–16	Lessons 1–3, 5–6, 8, 10, 15–16 ▪ Pre- and post-unit assessments ▪ Record sheets ▪ Notebook entries ▪ Class lists and discussions
Water pushes up on both floating and submerged objects with a buoyant force; objects push down on the water. Lessons 7–16	Lessons 8, 10, 15–16 ▪ Record sheets ▪ Notebook entries ▪ Class discussions
The buoyant force on large objects is greater than the buoyant force on smaller objects. Lessons 7–16	Lessons 8, 10, 15–16 ▪ Class discussions ▪ Notebook entries
The amount of water an object displaces is directly related to the object's volume. Lessons 9–16	Lessons 10, 16 ▪ Record sheets ▪ Small-group and class discussions ▪ Notebook entries
Because of buoyant force, objects appear to weigh less when they are submerged. Lessons 10–12, 15–16	Lessons 10, 15–16 ▪ Class discussions ▪ Notebook entries ▪ Record sheets
Objects that weigh more than the same volume of water sink; objects that weigh less than the same volume of water float. Lessons 12, 14–16	Lessons 15–16 ▪ Class discussions ▪ Notebook entries
Salt water weighs more than an equal amount of fresh water. Lessons 13–16	Lessons 15–16 ▪ Record sheets ▪ Notebook entries
The buoyancy of an object varies with the density of the liquid. Lessons 14–16	Lessons 15–16 ▪ Pre- and post-unit assessments ▪ Class lists ▪ Notebook entries

Skills	
Goals	**Assessment Strategies**
Observing, recording, and organizing test results. Lessons 1–16	Lessons 1–3, 5, 8, 10 ▪ Pre- and post-unit assessments ▪ Record sheets ▪ Notebook entries ▪ Student-made record sheets

Skills (continued)

Goals	Assessment Strategies
Applying previous experiences to make predictions. Lessons 1–16	Lessons 1–3, 6, 8, 10, 15–16 ▪ Pre- and post-unit assessments ▪ Record sheets ▪ Notebook entries ▪ Small-group and class discussions
Creating and analyzing graphs. Lessons 3, 5, 11–12, 14	Lessons 3, 10 ▪ Class and individual graphs ▪ Notebook entries ▪ Class discussions
Calibrating a spring scale and using it to measure the magnitude of a force. Lessons 4–6, 9–13, 16	Lessons 5, 10, 16 ▪ Observations of spring scales ▪ Record sheets ▪ Class graphs ▪ Observations of investigations
Reading science materials for information. Lessons 8, 10, 15	Lessons 10, 15 ▪ Class discussions ▪ Notebook entries ▪ Student self-assessment
Communicating results through writing and discussion. Lessons 1–16	Lessons 1–2, 5–6, 8, 10, 15–16 ▪ Pre- and post-unit assessments ▪ Record sheets ▪ Notebook entries
Solving a problem that requires the application of previously learned concepts and skills. Lessons 7–8, 16	Lessons 8, 16 ▪ Notebook entries ▪ Observations of boats ▪ Record sheets ▪ Notebook entries

Attitudes	
Goals	**Assessment Strategies**
Developing an interest in investigating floating, sinking, and related phenomena. Lessons 1–16	Lesson 16 ▪ Student self-assessment
Recognizing the importance of repeating a test or measurement and comparing results. Lessons 2–16	Lessons 3, 5, 10, 16 ▪ Class discussions ▪ Notebook entries ▪ Student self-assessment

continued from pg. 7

assessments are activities that occur naturally within the context of both the individual lesson and the unit as a whole; they are often indistinguishable from instructional activities. By providing structured activities and guidelines for assessing students' progress and thinking, embedded assessments contribute to an ongoing, detailed profile of growth. In many STC units, the last lesson is an embedded assessment that challenges students to synthesize and apply concepts or skills from the unit.

Appendix A contains several *additional assessments* that can be used to determine students' understanding after the unit has been completed. In these assessments, students may work with materials to solve problems, conduct experiments, or interpret and organize data. In grades three through six, they may also complete self-assessments or paper-and-pencil tests. When you are selecting additional assessments, consider using more than one assessment to give students with different learning styles opportunities to express their knowledge and skills.

Documenting Student Performance: In STC units, assessment is based on your recorded observations, students' work products, and oral communication. All these documentation methods combine to give you a comprehensive picture of each student's growth.

Teachers' *observations and anecdotal notes* often provide the most useful information about students' understanding, especially in the early grades when some students are not yet writing their ideas fluently. Because it is important to document observations used for assessment, teachers frequently keep note cards, journals, or checklists. Many lessons include guidelines to help you focus your observations. The blackline master on pg. 11 provides a format you may want to use or adapt for recording observations.

Work products, which include both what students write and what they make, indicate students' progress toward the goals of the unit. Children produce a variety of written materials during a unit. Record sheets, which include written observations, drawings, graphs, tables, and charts, are an important part of all STC units. They provide evidence of each student's ability to collect, record, and process information. Students' science journals are another type of work product. In grades one and two, journal writings are primarily suggested as extension activities in many lessons. Often a rich source of information for assessment, these journal writings reveal students' thoughts, ideas, and questions over time.

Students' written work products should be kept together in folders to document learning over the course of the unit. When students refer back to their work from previous lessons, they can reflect on their learning. In some cases, students do not write or draw well enough for their products to be used for assessment purposes, but their experiences do contribute to the development of scientific literacy.

Oral communication—what students say formally and informally in class and in individual sessions with you—is a particularly useful way to learn what students know. This unit provides your students with many opportunities to share and discuss their own ideas, observations, and opinions. Some young children may be experiencing such activities for the first time. Encourage students to participate in discussions, and stress that there are no right or wrong responses. Creating an environment in which students feel secure expressing their own ideas can stimulate rich and diverse discussions.

Individual and group presentations can give you insights about the meanings your students have assigned to procedures and concepts and about their confidence in their learning. In fact, a student's verbal description of a chart, experiment, or graph is frequently more useful for assessment than the product or results. Questions posed by other students following presentations provide yet another opportunity for you to gather information. Ongoing records of discussions and presentations should be a part of your documentation of students' learning.

Glossary

The glossary for this unit is provided as an additional resource for both teachers and students. The definitions are *not* unit specific and are intended to apply across the STC curriculum. The definitions are provided to facilitate discussion and may serve to enhance other unit activities. *Under no circumstances should students be required to memorize the terms or definitions presented in the glossary.*

Floating and Sinking: Observations of Student Performance

STUDENT'S NAME:	
Concepts	**Observations**
• Several variables affect the buoyancy of an object.	
• Water pushes up on both floating and submerged objects with a buoyant force; objects push down on the water.	
• The buoyant force on large objects is greater than the buoyant force on smaller objects.	
• The amount of water an object displaces is directly related to the object's volume.	
• Because of buoyant force, objects appear to weigh less when they are submerged.	
• Objects that weigh more than the same volume of water sink; objects that weigh less than the same volume of water float.	
• Salt water weighs more than an equal amount of fresh water.	
• The buoyancy of an object varies with the density of the liquid.	
Skills	
• Observing, recording, and organizing test results.	
• Applying previous experiences to make predictions.	
• Creating and analyzing graphs.	
• Calibrating a spring scale and using it to measure the magnitude of a force.	
• Reading science materials for information.	
• Communicating results through writing and discussion.	
• Solving a problem that requires the application of previously learned concepts and skills.	

What Do We Know about Floating and Sinking?

Overview and Objectives

What makes objects float? What makes objects sink? Students' responses to these questions provide you with a pre-unit assessment of their current knowledge of floating and sinking. Students are also challenged to explain a puzzling phenomenon: an object sinks in one container of liquid but floats in another. At the end of the unit, students revisit the activities, giving you an opportunity to assess their growth in understanding the concepts in this unit.

- Students prepare a science notebook that they will use to record their ideas throughout the unit.

- Students brainstorm why they think things float or sink.

- Students observe an object that both floats and sinks and then record their observations and ideas about how this could happen.

Background

People have been interested in the phenomena of floating and sinking for thousands of years. It seems straightforward: some things float while others sink. Several variables, however, contribute to whether an object floats or sinks. These include the object's size, weight, and design, as well as the density of liquid it is placed in.

Therefore, no single variable determines whether a particular object will float or sink. Still, many people look for simple rules to explain these phenomena. For example, it is not unusual to hear someone say, "Heavy objects sink; light objects float," or "All things made of plastic will float." But such statements are oversimplifications. It is not hard to find examples that contradict each generalization.

Over the course of the unit, students will investigate floating and sinking through a variety of activities. It is important that students actively construct their own explanations of the behavior of floating and sinking objects and the interactions between the objects and the liquids in which they are placed. As students begin to make sense of their observations, they will begin to identify the more important variables that contribute to the behavior of floating and sinking objects.

Students' ideas and the words they use to describe them will probably not resemble the carefully crafted definitions of scientists. But over time, the students' investigations will allow them to refine their ideas in a way that will give them increased understanding. This process of investigation will help students begin to recognize that they can figure things out for themselves.

In this first lesson, students are asked to observe and speculate about the behavior of an acrylic object that floats in salt water and sinks in fresh water. This activity is valuable as a pre-unit assessment because it provides an opportunity for the teacher to hear some of the ideas that students already have about floating and sinking. Some students will be very puzzled by their observations and may not be willing to even venture a guess to explain them. Other students may predict that one of the fluids is somehow different and is causing the object to behave differently. Still other students will suspect some sort of magic trick or some unseen attribute of the object.

All of these observations are useful pre-unit assessments. At the end of the unit, you will compare them to a post-unit assessment as a way to evaluate how students' thinking has changed as a result of their experiences in the unit.

Materials

For each student
- 1 science notebook
- 1 **Record Sheet 1-A: Recording Sheet**
- 1 resealable plastic bag

For every two students
- 1 *Floating and Sinking* Student Activity Book

For the class
- 2 plastic tubes, 4.5 × 16 cm (1¾ × 6″)
- 1 box of kosher salt, natural flake
- 2 white acrylic beads
- 1 plastic spoon
- 1 plastic tank
- Sheets of newsprint

Preparation

1. Pour water into one of the plastic tubes until it is approximately two-thirds full. Fill the other tube with the same amount of saturated salt water. Label the tubes "A" and "B" so that students can refer to them as the "unidentified liquids." Directions for preparing salt water are found on pgs. 18–19.

2. Place the acrylic bead in each of the tubes to check whether the object will float in the salt water and sink in the fresh water. To avoid splashing, you may want to use a spoon to place the object in the tube.

3. Make one copy of **Record Sheet 1-A: Recording Sheet** for each student.

4. Write the following questions on newsprint for the class brainstorming session. You may need several sheets for students' responses. (For more information about brainstorming, refer to Teaching *Floating and Sinking*, pg. 6.)

   ■ What do you think makes objects float or sink?

   ■ What questions do you have about floating and sinking?

Procedure

1. Have students prepare a science notebook, which they will use throughout the unit. Explain that the notebook will be a record of their thoughts and ideas. Then ask students to think about some reasons for writing down the date above each day's entry.

2. Ask students to write in their notebooks some thoughts about what makes objects float or sink.

3. Next, conduct a class brainstorming session. Ask students to respond to the questions listed on the newsprint sheets. These sheets are a useful way to pull together class discussions throughout the unit. Therefore, you will need to find a place in the classroom to post them. Let students know that they will revisit their questions and add new ideas as they progress through the unit.

Figure 1-1

Class
brainstorming
session

4. Distribute **Record Sheet 1-A: Recording Sheet.** Let students know that this is not a test but rather a record for them to refer to later on, after they have had a chance to work with the materials a little more.

5. Pass the acrylic beads around the class so that students may observe them closely.

6. Ask students to observe what happens as you place one acrylic bead in each of the tubes. Allow several minutes for them to record their observations and ideas. Encourage students to draw pictures as well as write sentences.

   Tell students to insert Record Sheet 1-A into their notebooks as the first entry. Explain that they will look back at their notebook entries later on to see how their ideas have changed.

7. Let the class know that they will be conducting more investigations that will help them explain the puzzling behavior of the bead in the two liquids.

Figure 1-2

The bead sinks in fresh water and floats in salt water

Final Activities

1. Distribute a resealable plastic bag to each student.

2. Ask students to use the bag to gather five objects they would like to test to see whether they float or sink in water.

   Explain that in the next lesson students will have an opportunity to make predictions about these objects and then test them.

Extensions

LANGUAGE ARTS

1. Students may be interested in how fish move in water. Ask students to write and illustrate a story or poem about a fish or other undersea creature and how it gets around.

LANGUAGE ARTS

2. Encourage students to read *Shark Lady,* by Ann McGovern, which tells the story of Eugenie Clark, a scientist who studies the behavior of sharks (see Appendix B: Bibliography).

Assessment

In this lesson, each student's notebook entries, **Record Sheet 1-A,** and the class brainstorming lists will enable you to assess students' knowledge about the variables that affect whether an object floats or sinks. This information serves as the first part of the matched pre- and post-unit assessments, which are integral to teaching the unit. The post-unit assessment is on pg. 145, following Lesson 16.

To help you keep track of information about each student, record informal observations on charts, cards, or Post-it™ notes. As you review notebook entries, Record Sheet 1-A, and the class brainstorming lists, keep the following questions in mind:

- What information do students have about why objects float or sink?

- What variables (if any) are mentioned?

- Do students discuss or question both the object and the liquid?

- Were individual students able to provide reasons why the acrylic bead floated in one liquid but not in the other? What prior experiences were used to defend reasons?

Throughout the unit, students will also be using important skills basic to science: observing, recording, comparing, analyzing, and predicting. You can assess students' growth in using these process skills by observing and talking to students as they work and by looking at individual written work. Combining information gained from both strategies will provide a complete assessment profile. In this lesson, look for the following:

- The detail students use when writing their ideas and questions

- The inclusion of a reason when making predictions

- The observations included in their explanations of the bead's behavior

In the section Teaching *Floating and Sinking,* on pgs. 5–11, you will find a detailed discussion about the assessment of students' learning. The specific goals and related assessments for this unit are summarized in Figure T-2, on pgs. 10–11. Please keep in mind that some fifth-graders may not completely understand every concept listed. As you continue through this unit, look for students' development in understanding the concepts rather than mastery of them.

Instructions for Preparing Concentrated Salt Water

1. In order to conduct the demonstration in Step 6 of the **Procedure** section, you will need a mixture of concentrated salt water for one tube and an equal amount of fresh water for the other.

   The tubes and the liquid in them should appear to be as nearly identical as possible.

2. Prepare the salt water by mixing one part salt with four parts cool water in a large container.

   If you are using the plastic cups, which are 300 ml (10 oz), add half a cup of salt to 2 cups of water.

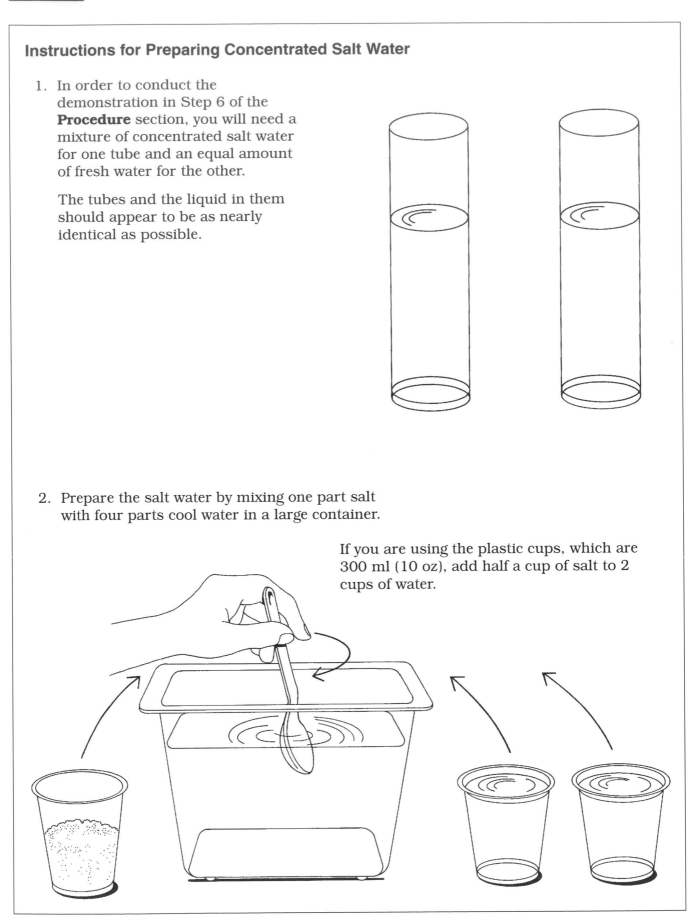

3. Stir the saltwater mixture until all of the salt dissolves. If the salt has not completely dissolved after five minutes of stirring, pour the salt water into another container, leaving the undissolved salt behind.

4. Test the salt water by placing the acrylic bead in the salt water and observing whether it floats or sinks.

   If the bead floats, cover the salt water until it is needed for the demonstration. If the bead sinks, add a little more salt and continue stirring the mixture until the water is salty enough to make the bead float.

Notes

■ If the salt water is left standing for several hours, salt crystals may begin forming. The crystals can be dissolved by vigorous stirring, or they can be removed with a spoon before you conduct the demonstration.

■ Check to see whether the acrylic bead will float in the salt water after it has been left standing.

■ To reduce evaporation, keep the salt water covered when not in use.

■ Save all the salt water for use later in the unit. Keep it in a covered container.

Record Sheet 1-A

Name: _____

Date: _____

Recording Sheet

What did you see happening?

What are at least two reasons you can think of for what you observed?

1. _____
   _____
   _____
   _____

2. _____
   _____
   _____
   _____

3. _____
   _____
   _____
   _____

Making and Testing Predictions about Familiar Objects

Overview and Objectives

Students begin their investigation of buoyancy, the tendency of an object to float, by making and testing predictions about the variety of objects they have collected. This experience will give students a chance to become familiar with the process they will use throughout the unit: predicting whether objects will float or sink, explaining why they think so, and testing their predictions. As students go through this process and explain their reasoning, you will gain insights into their ideas about floating and sinking.

- Students make predictions and explain their thinking about whether a variety of objects will float or sink.

- Students test their predictions and record results.

- Students discuss their observations and ideas about whether the objects float or sink.

Background

Two of the characteristics that affect floating and sinking are easily measured—the weight and the size of objects. For instance, a ship doesn't float "because it is light"; rather, it floats because its weight and size act together so that the water (or other liquid it is floating in) pushes up on the ship with a force equal to the force of gravity pulling down on it. The upward push of the water depends on the amount of space the ship occupies under water, and it is called the **buoyant force.**

As students begin to recognize the buoyant force, they often refer to it as the **floating force.** Either term can be used to refer to this phenomenon.

It is a challenging task to predict whether an object will float or sink. Students will use many strategies to make such predictions. Some make predictions based on the material the object is made of, or on their previous experiences with similar objects. Others will focus on the object's size, shape, weight, or some other single characteristic of the object.

As students gain experience sorting out the possible reasons why an object floats or sinks, they may begin to consider the effect of combinations of characteristics. For example, a student might say that a piece of charcoal floats because it is "light and big," instead of merely saying, "It's a floater," or "It's light."

This lesson presents another opportunity to assess the ideas that students have at the beginning of the unit. Later lessons will provide experiences that encourage students to look at the causes of floating and sinking in a variety of ways as they move toward a deeper understanding of these phenomena.

Materials

For each student
  1   science notebook
  1   resealable plastic bag containing student-collected objects
  1   **Record Sheet 2-A: Prediction Record**

For every two students
  1   plastic tank with 2 liters (2 qt) of water
  1   plastic plate
  1   towel

For the class
  6   plastic buckets with handles, 4 liters (1 gal)
  6   sponges
      Several sheets of newsprint
      Class brainstorming list (from Lesson 1)

Preparation

1. Decide how to manage the task of filling and emptying the plastic tanks in your room. You may want to ask students to help.

Figure 2-1

Working with water in the classroom

2. Water is a challenge to work with in the classroom, so you probably will want to set up a special system of rules and procedures to help students work with it successfully. Some suggestions are listed on Figure 2-2. The plastic plates will help contain some of the minor splashes and spills.

Figure 2-2

Rules for working with water

3. Make one copy of **Record Sheet 2-A** for each student.

4. Decide how you want to pair students for their investigations of the objects they have gathered.

Procedure

1. Ask students the following question: "What is the difference between a prediction and a guess?" (A prediction is based on observations or experience, while a guess is not. Most students are probably familiar with predictions that meteorologists make about the weather. They also may know the basis for some of the predictions, such as radar observations, temperature readings, and satellite photographs.) Then discuss with students one reason for writing down predictions: to enable them to make comparisons with what actually happens.

2. Distribute **Record Sheet 2-A.** Ask students to list the objects they have selected.

3. Ask students to write their predictions on Record Sheet 2-A, along with their reasons for making each prediction. You may want to provide students with a sample format for making predictions and giving reasons, such as the following:

"I predict that _____ (this toothbrush) will _____ (float/sink) because _____ (it is made of plastic and is long and skinny.)"

4. As students complete their predictions, distribute the tanks of water to each pair. Ask students to test their objects one at a time. Remind students to record what they find out on Record Sheet 2-A.

Figure 2-3

Filling out Record Sheet 2-A

5. Ask students to return the water to the storage area or sink and place the test objects back in the bag. Have them leave the bags unsealed so that the objects will dry.

Management Tip: You will probably want to reuse 15 of the bags for storage of the test objects that student pairs will begin working with in the next lesson.

Final Activities

1. Ask students what surprised them as they tested their objects. Encourage them to share what they learned and how they might change their ideas about certain objects.

2. As in Lesson 1, ask students, "What do you think makes some things float and other things sink?" Encourage the class to add to the brainstorming list some new explanations for why some objects float and other objects sink. This list will be useful as a reference in later lessons, after students have had additional experiences with floating and sinking.

Figure 2-4

Additions to the brainstorming list from Lesson 1

WHAT DO YOU THINK MAKES OBJECTS FLOAT OR SINK?

3/9 •Heavy things sink, but not always.

•Air inside makes things float.

•Fish float after they die.

3/11 •Plastic floats if the water doesn't get over it or in it.

•Big things sink unless they are light.

•Boats float because the sides keep the water out.

Assessment

When you review **Record Sheet 2-A,** consider the following questions:

- How well were students able to provide reasons for their predictions?

- Are the reasons plausible? Do students mention any characteristics of the objects, such as size, weight, or design?

Revisiting the brainstorming list and adding to it throughout the unit is one way to monitor students' changing ideas. The post-unit assessment, on pg. 145, includes suggestions for analyzing the list with your class.

Record Sheet 2-A

Name: _____

Date: _____

Prediction Record

Name of the Object	My Prediction and Some Reasons	What Happened: F–It floated S–It sank

Which Things Float?
Which Things Sink?

Overview and Objectives

To expand their understanding of their observations in Lesson 2, students begin exploring variables that affect buoyancy. Using a set of 14 objects that vary in weight, size, design, and material, students focus on the effect that weight and size have on whether an object floats or sinks. In this lesson, students' predictions of the weight of each object in relation to the others sets the stage for them to develop a method to measure the weights of the objects in the next two lessons.

- Students make predictions and explain their thinking about whether each object in a set will float or sink.

- Students test their predictions and record results.

- Students discuss and compare the results of their investigations.

- Students apply results of the floating test to rank the objects from lightest to heaviest.

Background

Over the next five lessons, students will be observing the effect that the variables of weight, size, and design have on whether an object floats or sinks. Students' observations may change some of their ideas about which objects float and which sink.

For example, although many students may have noticed that heavy ships float and lightweight coins sink, they may still hold fast to the idea that heavy things sink and light things float. This idea is supported by other experiences: most students have observed that rocks sink, while paper cups, feathers, and balloons all float. The simplicity of this idea makes it a powerful concept in students' minds.

Another reason that students hold on to this simple rule is that they can usually generate explanations for any exceptions. For example, students may explain the fact that some heavy things, such as ships and bottles, float by saying they have air in them, an idea that is also supported by student observations. While this is a reasonable explanation in many cases—as is the idea about heavy and light objects—it is not the whole story. Some solid objects, such as the polyethylene cylinder, do not contain air but still float. In this lesson, students will see this for themselves.

Encouraging students to consider adopting new theories in light of new experiences is a challenging and fascinating process. By giving students many opportunities to make and test predictions and to try out their ideas with other students, you can help them construct new explanations for what they have observed.

The objects used in this lesson have been chosen to provide a variety of materials, shapes, and weights for students to investigate. The two sets of cylinders provide a range of weights while keeping size and shape constant. The wood bead surprises many students because it floats even though it has a hole in it. The fishing bobber floats, although it is heavier than the aluminum nut and marble, which sink. The ball of clay sinks, but in later lessons students will learn that it can be made to float. And the nylon bolt sinks in fresh water, but it will float in salt water when tested again in Lesson 14. Experiences with these objects in subsequent lessons will build upon today's predicting and testing activities.

In this lesson, students begin to construct a class graph showing the weights of the objects. They will add to it in Lessons 5, 11, 12, and 14. This class graph is an important part of the unit. It enables students to reflect on what they have observed. Once completed, it illustrates one way to predict whether an object will float or sink—by comparing the weight of an object with the weight of an equal amount of water. If the object weighs less than an equal amount of water, it will float. If it weighs more, it will sink.

Materials

For each student

    1   science notebook

    1   **Record Sheet 3-A: Prediction Record**

For every two students

    1   set of 14 objects: large and small cylinders made of aluminum, acrylic (clear plastic), wood, and polyethylene; a fishing bobber; a nylon bolt; an aluminum nut; a ball of clay; a marble; and a wood bead

    1   plastic tank with 2 liters (2 qt) of water

    1   plastic plate

    1   towel

For the class

    1   set of object cards (blackline masters in Appendix C)

    2   equal-arm balances

    6   sponges

        Jumbo paper clips (optional)

Figure 3-1

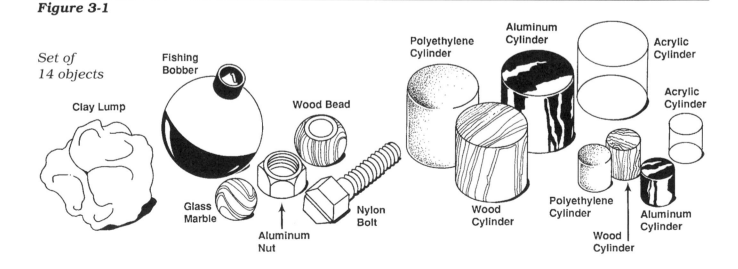

Set of 14 objects

Clay Lump — Fishing Bobber — Wood Bead — Glass Marble — Aluminum Nut — Nylon Bolt — Polyethylene Cylinder — Aluminum Cylinder — Acrylic Cylinder — Acrylic Cylinder — Wood Cylinder — Polyethylene Cylinder — Wood Cylinder — Aluminum Cylinder

Preparation

1. Arrange the materials for easy distribution to students. You may want to set up a cafeteria-style system.

2. Because students will be using the objects in many lessons, it is a good idea to store them as a set in resealable bags. Decide whether you (and volunteers) will take care of storage, or whether students will do it themselves.

3. Divide the clay into equal lumps, each of which weighs about the same as 20 to 22 jumbo paper clips as measured with the equal-arm balance. The combined weight of the large acrylic cylinder, large wood cylinder, and small aluminum cylinder also equals approximately 22 paper clips (see Figure 3-2).

   Use the balance to ensure that each student gets about the same amount of clay. You may want to enlist a student helper to assist with this task.

   Note: If your students have not worked with clay before, you may want to explain that it is easier to work with if they remove tiny air (and water) pockets. Students can do this by kneading the clay into a uniform lump. The "need to knead" will become apparent to them as they work with these materials.

Figure 3-2

Weighing the lumps of clay

4. Make one copy of **Record Sheet 3-A** for each student.

5. Duplicate one set of blackline masters (Appendix C) to use in Step 2 of the **Final Activities** section.

Management Tip: Because of the number of objects students are testing, this lesson probably will take longer than one class period to complete.

Procedure

1. Review with students the predict-and-test process they used in Lesson 2. Then introduce them to the new set of objects. Explain that they will be investigating the floating and sinking properties of these objects over the next few weeks.

2. Distribute **Record Sheet 3-A** to students. Ask them to work with a partner to make predictions based on what they can observe about whether they think the objects will sink or float. Remind them to record their predictions along with the reasons for them. Tell students that these reasons will provide a record of their thinking, which they can refer to later to see if their ideas have changed as a result of their investigations.

3. After students have finished recording their predictions and reasons, distribute the materials to each pair of students. Ask them to test their predictions by placing the objects in water to see which float and which sink. Ask students to record the results on Record Sheet 3-A.

4. After students have finished testing, ask them to return their materials to the storage area. Students who finish early can work in small groups to compare their results.

Final Activities

1. Ask students to think about their observations. Then have them write in their science notebooks about the observations that surprised them as well as the outcomes they expected.

2. To focus the discussion on the results of the investigation, hold up a card with the name and picture of each object. (Use the blackline masters, found in Appendix C, for this activity.) Ask students what they observed when they tested each object. If there is disagreement about what happened, encourage some students to repeat the test. Once agreement has been reached, indicate whether the objects floated or sank in water by underlining the word on the card with different-colored markers. For example, you could underline objects that sank with blue and those that floated with red.

3. Now, ask the class to make predictions about which objects are heavier and which are lighter. First, ask students to indicate which of the objects they think is the lightest. Then have them predict the order of the rest of the objects from lightest to heaviest. Record these class predictions by posting the cards in a row from lightest to heaviest on the wall or bulletin board (see Figure 3-3). This will be the beginning of a class graph used also in Lessons 5, 11, 12, and 14.

4. Explain to students that they will have a chance to use a spring scale to test these predictions for themselves in Lesson 5.

Extension

```
SCIENCE
```

Encourage students to try to fasten together pairs of objects in various ways and test which combinations float and which sink. Ask students to record their observations. It is particularly interesting to fasten together a floater and a sinker.

Figure 3-3

Class predictions about weight

Assessment

1. When you review **Record Sheet 3-A,** consider the following questions:

   ■ Are students including plausible reasons for their predictions? Do the reasons reflect the students' experiences in Lesson 2?

   ■ Are the students' reasons becoming more detailed? For instance, "because it is plastic" might be a legitimate reason for predicting that an object will either float or sink, but "because it is made of a kind of plastic that floats" is a more detailed reason for predicting that an object will float.

   ■ Are students including more than one reason for their predictions?

2. Old ideas often give way slowly to new ideas. Look for signs that students are receptive to the new information they have gathered from their observations. One way to do this is to ask students about any surprises they found while investigating. Some students may have difficulty accepting the fact that some of their predictions did not match their observations. Encourage students to view this as a positive way to learn new things, and not as a "failed test."

Record Sheet 3-A

Name: _____

Date: _____

Prediction Record

Name of the Object	My Prediction and Some Reasons	What Happened: F–It floated S–It sank
Aluminum Nut		
Wood Bead		
Glass Marble		
Fishing Bobber		
Nylon Bolt		

Record Sheet 3-A (continued)

Name: _____

Date: _____

Prediction Record

Name of the Object	My Prediction and Some Reasons	What Happened: F–It floated S–It sank
Large Acrylic Cylinder		
Large Aluminum Cylinder		
Large Polyethylene Cylinder		
Large Wood Cylinder		

Record Sheet 3-A (continued)

Name: _____

Date: _____

Prediction Record

Name of the Object	My Prediction and Some Reasons	What Happened: F–It floated S–It sank
Clay		
Small Acrylic Cylinder		
Small Aluminum Cylinder		
Small Polyethylene Cylinder		
Small Wood Cylinder		

Measuring Weight with a Spring Scale

Overview and Objectives

In the last lesson, students began investigating the effect that the variable of weight has on whether an object floats or sinks. In this lesson, students are introduced to a tool for measuring weight—the spring scale. Through the process of calibrating the scale, students begin to connect the concept of weight to units used to represent weight. In later lessons, students will use this tool to find approximate measures for the weights of objects and to help them investigate any connection between an object's weight and the buoyant force on the object.

- Students calibrate a spring scale with paper clips.

- Students practice weighing with the calibrated spring scales.

- Students compare their results and discuss their observations.

Background

The **weight,** or downward force, on any object is caused by the attraction between the mass of the earth and the mass of the object. This attraction is called **gravity.**

The weight of an object can be measured by a number of methods. A balance, such as the equal-arm balance shown in Figure 4-1, can be used to weigh an object by comparing its weight with standard weights placed on the opposite side of the balance.

Spring scales, however, work differently. Instead of measuring weight by comparison to a standard, spring scales measure weight by stretching a spring; the heavier the object placed on the spring scale, the more the spring stretches. Although many spring scales are calibrated in grams or ounces when they are manufactured, students will calibrate the spring scales provided in this unit by using jumbo paper clips as standard weights. They will do this by marking the length of the stretched spring for one paper clip, two paper clips, and so on.

There are several reasons why it is important for students to calibrate their own spring scales. The process of calibration will help students better understand the relationship between the **concept** of weight and the numbers and units used to **represent** weight when making measurements. Although there will be variations in measurements with the student-calibrated scales, you probably will find that these variations are an effective way to promote comparisons and discussions of the measurements made throughout the unit. Through recalibrating their scales, students will discover that this process is one way to try to achieve more consistent measurements.

Figure 4-1

Weighing a peach with an equal-arm balance

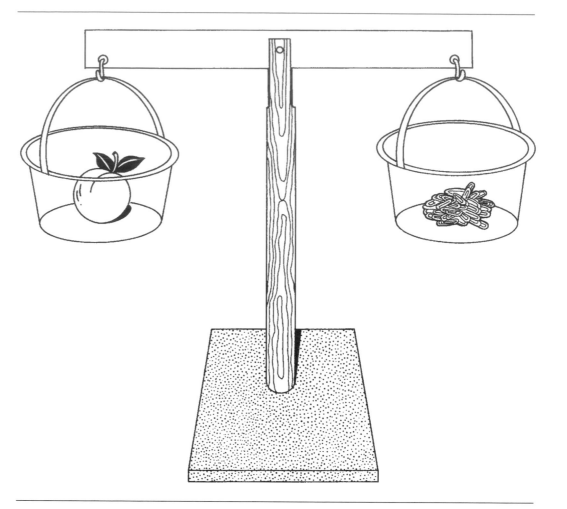

Once calibrated, a spring scale can be used to measure the weight, or downward force (pull) of gravity, on an object. It also can be used to measure pushes and pulls in other directions. For example, the spring scale can be used to investigate the upward buoyant force of water on an object. In later lessons, students will use the spring scale to measure both the weight of objects and the buoyant force of water on objects.

The spring scale introduced in this lesson has several characteristics that make it a good choice for this unit. It has a plastic spring that stretches for a wide range of weights and will not corrode when exposed to salt water. The spring is sensitive enough to calibrate with paper clips yet strong enough to weigh the large aluminum cylinder.

However, the plastic spring does have one curious characteristic that you need to be aware of. It "creeps" when fully stretched for longer than a few seconds. As a result, it takes several seconds for the spring to come to rest when weighing a heavy object and several seconds for it to "creep" back to zero when the heavy object is removed. For example, a lump of clay might stretch the spring as much as 20 paper clips when first loaded on the hook, but then slowly creep to indicate 22 paper clips. When unloaded, the scale may indicate 1 or 2 clips until enough time has passed for it to creep back to zero. Students will need to make allowances for this when weighing heavy objects.

Note: Some students have found that a light tap on the side of the spring scale speeds the creeping.

Figure 4-2

*Calibrating a
spring scale*

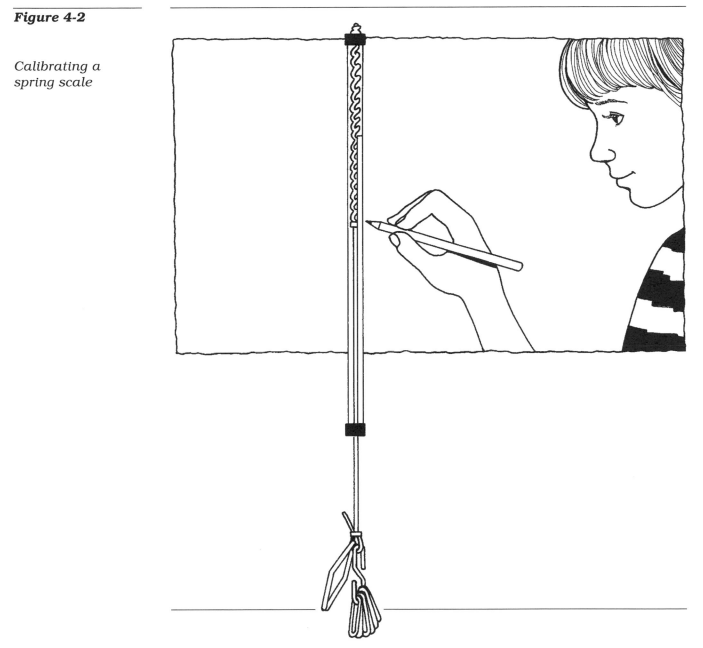

Materials

For each student
  1   science notebook

For every two students
  1   spring scale
  1   piece of masking tape, 1.25 x 30 cm (½ × 12″)
  1   large bobby pin
  30   jumbo paper clips
  1   small resealable bag
  1   ball of clay (from Lesson 3)

For the class
  2   equal-arm balances
     Newsprint

Preparation

1. Attach a piece of masking tape to the side of each of the spring scales. In Step 4 of the **Procedure** section, students will calibrate the spring scale by marking on this tape.

2. Prepare a resealable bag containing 30 jumbo paper clips for each pair of students.

Procedure

1. Ask students to review the class prediction made in Lesson 3 of the order of the objects from lightest to heaviest. If students want to change their predictions, or if they have made different predictions from those made by the class in Lesson 3, ask them to record their new ideas in their notebooks. Questions such as the following may help focus the discussion:

   ■ What are some reasons for your predictions?

   ■ What are some ways you can test your predictions?

2. Distribute the spring scales to each pair of students. Encourage students to explore the scales.

3. After a few minutes, ask students to put the spring scales aside while they help you make a list on newsprint of the characteristics of the spring scale that they have just observed.

4. Explain to students that in order to use these scales to measure weight it is necessary to calibrate them. A good way to do this is by using paper clips as standard weights. Ask students to discuss the advantages of using paper clips, which all weigh nearly the same, instead of other objects, which might vary in weight. Then have students follow the directions in the Student Activity Book (pgs. 11–12) to calibrate the spring scale (see Figure 4–2). These directions are also reproduced on pgs. 46–47 in the Teacher's Guide.

Final Activities

1. Once students have calibrated their scales, challenge them to use the scales to weigh (in clips) a ball of clay. Encourage student pairs to exchange clay so that they can compare their measurements.

2. Invite students to break the clay into smaller pieces for additional practice in using the spring scale. Again, encourage them to compare and discuss their results.

3. Invite students to check their results with the equal-arm balance, using paper clips as standard weights. If there are any variations in results, have students discuss the possible reasons and, if necessary, recalibrate their spring scales.

   Note: Measurements may vary because of inconsistent markings on the scales. It is a valuable exercise for students to recalibrate their spring scales. Not only does recalibrating help students better understand the process, but it also helps ensure consistency of the measurements.

Extensions

LANGUAGE ARTS

1. Ask students to write and illustrate a story about a scale they have seen being used to weigh something. If students have trouble thinking of a scale, suggest that they focus on scales they've seen in a store, a doctor's office, or at weigh stations along the highway.

SCIENCE

2. Ask students to weigh eight sheets of notebook paper. Ask students to predict and test the weight of four sheets, two sheets, and one sheet. After they have made predictions, challenge them to find the weight of 35 sheets.

SCIENCE

3. Encourage pairs of students to use the spring scale to predict how many sheets of paper are in a pile. They can test their predictions by counting the sheets. Encourage students to keep a record of each investigation.

LANGUAGE ARTS   MATHEMATICS

4. Ask students to write and illustrate a series of comparison sentences about weight. You may want to help them get started by giving them an example, such as the following:

    ■ A liter of water is heavy, but a bowling ball is heavier.

    ■ A car is lighter than an elephant but heavier than a bicycle.

Student Instructions for Calibrating the Spring Scale

1. Have one partner hold the spring scale straight up and down. Hang the bobby pin on the loop at the bottom. The bobby pin is a part of the spring scale that can be used to hold objects that are being weighed.

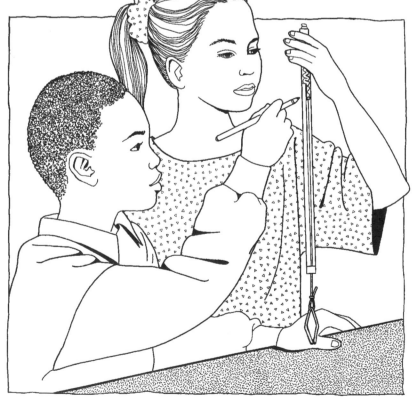

2. To make the "0" mark, hold the scale so the metal pointer is at your eye level. Make a mark on the masking tape at the level of the metal pointer. Call this mark "0" to indicate "no paper clips."

3. Next, bend one paper clip into a hook. Hang the paper clip through the loop. Make a mark on the masking tape across from the pointer. Label this mark "1" to indicate "one paper clip."

4. Add another paper clip so that there are two paper clips on the spring scale. Make a mark on the masking tape and label it "2."

5. Keep adding paper clips, making marks, and labeling each mark until your spring scale is calibrated.

6. On the masking tape, put your initials and the date that you calibrated the spring scale.

Weighing Floaters and Sinkers

Overview and Objectives

Using their calibrated spring scales, students measure the weights of the objects from Lesson 3 and compare them with their predictions of relative weights. Graphing the data helps the class discover that small objects can be heavier than large ones. Students build on this discovery in Lessons 6 through 8 as they explore the effects of size, weight, and design on buoyancy.

- Students use the spring scale to weigh their collection of objects.

- Students compare and discuss results and determine an average measure of weight for each object.

- Students create a class graph to show the weights of all the objects.

- Students compare size with weight and discuss any questions raised.

Background

During today's lesson, students will be measuring weight with a spring scale. Because the spring scales are of limited precision, you should anticipate that the measurements students get will often vary by at least one "clip," with greater variation likely.

Students often attribute a greater degree of accuracy to their measurements than is realistic. They often think that their readings are "exact" and that their measurements are "right," while everyone else's are "wrong." Therefore, it is important to discuss the appropriate level of precision that students can expect with the spring scale—variation by at least one clip—and determine a strategy the class can use to agree on an "average" weight.

There are three basic strategies students can use to decide which number best represents the average weight of each object. A line plot will illustrate the range of measurements as well as the **mode,** the weight obtained by the greatest number of students (see Figure 5-1). The middle, or **median,** weight can also be found easily on a line plot simply by counting the number of responses until you reach the "middle" one. For example, if a line plot shows responses from 15 groups, then the eighth number would be considered the median. The **mean,** or arithmetic average, can be found by using a calculator to add all the measurements that students obtained and then dividing by the number of measurements. This approach, however, creates a problem. The arithmetic calculation of the mean often results in a fractional number. Because the spring scale is calibrated with paper clips, a fractional number is meaningless. For this reason, the median or the mode is a more appropriate average in this unit.

Figure 5-1

Sample line plot

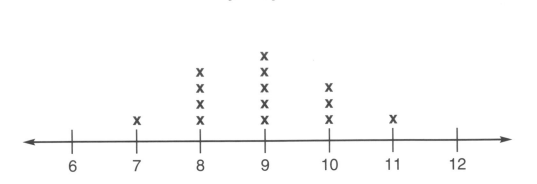

Acrylic Cylinder

Weight in Paper Clips

Mrs. O'Conner's fifth-grade class
April 1995

Materials

For each student

   1   science notebook
   1   **Record Sheet 5-A: Recording Measurements**

For every two students

   1   calibrated spring scale
   1   set of 14 objects (from Lesson 3)
 35   No. 1 paper clips

For the class

   2   equal-arm balances
   1   set of object cards (from Lesson 3)

Preparation

1. Make one copy of **Record Sheet 5-A** for each student.

2. Arrange the materials for efficient distribution.

3. Decide how you will assign the objects to students to make the class graph in the **Final Activities** section.

Procedure

1. Review with students the class predictions about relative weight that were made in Lesson 3. Explain that in this lesson they will have a chance to use the spring scales they calibrated to measure the weight of each object and to compare their weights with their predictions.

2. Distribute **Record Sheet 5-A** to each student. Have students use it to keep a record of the weights. Remind them to weigh each object three times.

Management Tip: It may be helpful to provide time for students to practice this skill, perhaps in a designated area of the classroom that has a variety of things to weigh. In addition, it may be a good idea to include a recording chart in this area so that students can compare the results of their investigations with those of other students.

Figure 5-2

*Weighing objects
with the spring
scale*

3. Next, distribute the materials to students. The bobby-pin clip can be used to hold the objects, as shown in Figure 5-2. Encourage students to take turns reading the spring scale to check the measurements.

4. After students have finished weighing the objects and checking their measurements, ask them to return all the materials except the small paper clips to the storage area.

Final Activities

1. Assign an object to each pair of students. Ask each pair to determine the average weight for that object. To do this, students need to find out the weights the other groups came up with and then use one of the strategies described in the **Background** section.

2. Ask students to help you make a class graph showing the weights of the objects. In Lesson 3, students predicted the order of the objects from lightest to heaviest and recorded their predictions by posting the object cards. Now, have each pair of students hang the number of paper clips above each object card that equals the object's average weight in clips. Then rearrange the object cards so that they are posted from lightest to heaviest. Figure 5-4 shows what a class graph looks like.

Management Tip: To construct the class graph, use the smaller No. 1 paper clips; they fit comfortably on a standard-sized bulletin board.

Figure 5-3

Discovering
variations in
measurements

3. Ask students to think about what they now know about the relative size and weight of each object. Then have them write their ideas in their science notebooks. Were they surprised that some of the smaller objects were heavier than the large ones?

4. Ask students to think about what they now know about the relationship of relative weight to floating and sinking. Again, have them write their ideas in their science notebooks. Were they surprised by any of their findings?

Management Tip: Leave the graph on the wall. It will be used in later lessons.

Extensions

LANGUAGE ARTS

1. Ask students to make a list of descriptive adjectives for each of the objects in the set. Have them keep this list in their notebooks and add to it as they investigate new characteristics of floating and sinking. This list will be a helpful reference for students when they write or talk about the objects they are working with.

MATHEMATICS

2. Explore the concept of average with the class. Create lists of examples that illustrate each of the three averages—mean, median, and mode. Discuss appropriate uses for each type of average.

Figure 5-4

*Graphing the
weight of each
object*

Assessment

When you review the students' and class's products in this lesson, consider the following questions.

Record Sheet 5-A

- How well are students able to use the spring scale to get consistent measurements?

- Are students beginning to recognize the importance of validating test results?

Class Graph

- How well are students able to average the weight of an object?

Student Notebook Entries

- What information do students now have about the relationship between the size and weight of an object?

- What ideas do students have about the relationship of sinkers to relative weight?

Note: In the **Assessment** section of Lesson 2, it is suggested that students periodically review and add to the brainstorming lists begun in Lesson 1. The end of this lesson may be a productive point to revisit these lists and to ask students to consider once again the question "What do you think makes objects float or sink?"

Record Sheet 5-A

Name: _____

Date: _____

Recording Measurements

Name of the Object	Float (F) or Sink (S)	Weight in Clips		
		First Measurement	Second Measurement	Third Measurement
Aluminum Nut				
Wood Bead				
Glass Marble				
Fishing Bobber				
Nylon Bolt				
Clay				
Small Acrylic Cylinder				

Record Sheet 5-A (continued)

Name: _____

Date: _____

Recording Measurements

Name of the Object	Float (F) or Sink (S)	Weight in Clips		
		First Measurement	Second Measurement	Third Measurement
Small Aluminum Cylinder				
Small Polyethylene Cylinder				
Small Wood Cylinder				
Large Acrylic Cylinder				
Large Aluminum Cylinder				
Large Polyethylene Cylinder				
Large Wood Cylinder				

Making a Sinker Float

Overview and Objectives

In Lessons 4 and 5, students explored whether an object's size determined its weight. This lesson challenges and expands students' thinking about the effects of weight and size on buoyancy. They now investigate what happens when they change the shape of a clay ball to make the clay float rather than sink. As students do this activity, they are introduced to the concept of conservation—that is, changing the shape of clay does not change its amount or its weight. Through their experiences in this lesson, students begin to gain evidence that weight, size, and design affect buoyancy.

- Students investigate whether changing the shape of a piece of clay has an effect on its weight.

- Students explore ways to change the shape of a ball of clay so that the clay floats.

- Students discuss and compare the designs of their clay boats.

Background

Some students believe that by changing the shape of a piece of clay they may be able to change its weight. In this lesson, however, they observe that the weight of the clay remains the same when its shape is changed.

For some students, this experience will be enough to change their thinking and will show them that mass is conserved when the shape of the clay is changed. For others, however, even direct observation will not change their view. But over time, with more experiences, students will come to understand this concept.

Even though the weight of the clay does not change, your students will discover that it is possible to make it float by changing its shape. When the clay is molded into the shape of a hollow boat, it can be made to occupy a larger amount of space under water, which increases its buoyancy. If the clay boat has a large flat bottom and high sides, it will displace more water and therefore be able to hold more marbles.

Clay is a good material to use in exploring these ideas. For one thing, students can manipulate its shape and size on their own. Another advantage of clay is that it ordinarily sinks in water, but it can be made to float.

After students have had experience with these activities, they may begin to see that the phenomena of floating and sinking involve more than just weight.

Figure 6-1

Clay shapes that float or sink

Materials

For each student

    1   science notebook

    1   lump of clay, 30 g (1 oz, or 20 to 22 clips)

For every two students

    1   spring scale

    1   plastic tank with 2 liters (2 qt) of water

    1   plastic plate

    1   towel

For the class

    6   sponges

        Newsprint list of student ideas (from Lesson 2)

Preparation

1. If you need fresh clay, refer to Lesson 3, Step 3 of the **Preparation** section.

2. Post the brainstorming list begun in Lesson 1. This list reflects students' ideas about why some objects float while others sink. It will be used for the review in Step 1 of the **Procedure** section.

3. Arrange for the distribution of the water and other materials.

Procedure

1. Ask students what they discovered when they weighed the objects in Lesson 5. Also, ask them to look at the brainstorming list they worked on in Lessons 1 and 2. Ask students to share any new ideas they may have about the causes of floating and sinking.

2. Ask students to discuss their ideas about weight and the effect it has on floating and sinking. Questions such as the following may help get the discussion started:

   ■ What do you think caused some of the heavier objects that were weighed in Lesson 5 to float?

   ■ What do you think caused some of the lighter objects to sink?

3. Discuss with students whether they think adding or removing clay would affect how much the clay weighs. Then ask students if they think the weight of the clay would be affected if they changed its shape from a ball to a "pancake" or a "sausage." Distribute the clay and spring scales. Have teams of two students work on this problem by using the spring scale to compare the weights of the different shapes they create.

Management Tip: Remind students of the "need to knead" to make the clay easier to work with.

4. Ask students to record the weights of the different shapes of clay in their notebooks.

Figure 6-2

Weighing different shapes of clay

5. Ask students to put the clay and spring scales aside for a moment. Discuss what they found out about the weights of the different shapes. Give students time to express their ideas about why they think all of the different shapes—the ball, the pancake, and the sausage—weigh about the same amount.

6. When students have reached agreement that all of the shapes weigh about the same, ask them, "Do you think you can make the clay float by changing its shape? Why do you think so?"

7. Challenge the class to create as many shapes as possible that will float in water. Then distribute the water and other materials that the students will need to test their shapes.

Final Activities

1. After students have found several shapes that will float, ask them to draw and describe in their notebooks which shapes floated best and which shapes did not float at all.

2. Encourage students to share with each other the boat designs that floated. Ask them to share their drawings and descriptions and to look for similarities among the various designs.

3. Ask students to return the materials to the storage area and help dry off any water that may have dripped.

Extensions

ART   SCIENCE

1. Encourage students to draw a design for a boat. Ask them to include labels that explain some of the details of the boat—how it is propelled, what materials it is made of, and what the boat will be used for.

SCIENCE

2. Ask students to bring in objects or pictures of objects that float, such as different types of boats. Have students compare the designs and shapes. How are they alike? How are they different?

Assessment

As you reflect on the classroom discussion and review the students' notebook entries, consider the following questions:

- Are students becoming aware that the design of an object can affect whether it floats or sinks?

- Are students able to identify new variables that affect whether an object floats or sinks?

- How well are students able to identify the similarities among the boat designs that floated and those that sank?

- How well are students able to identify the differences among the boat designs that floated and those that sank?

Investigating Boat Designs

Overview and Objectives

In the last lesson, students began investigating the effect of different designs on an object's buoyancy when the weight is constant. Now they apply the results of that investigation as they test designs in an effort to increase buoyancy. Using marbles as cargo, students compare the number of marbles each design will support to determine the efficiency of the designs. This activity sets the stage for testing the effect of size in the next lesson.

■ Students create their own record charts.

■ Students investigate and record how many marbles different clay boats can keep afloat.

■ Students record and discuss their observations about design.

Background

The buoyant force on an object depends on the amount of space that the object occupies under water. When the amount of space under water is increased, the buoyant force is also increased. In this lesson, students investigate this effect quantitatively. They do this by measuring the cargo that various designs of clay boats can support. (The weight of the clay has not been changed; only its shape has been modified.) The boats that hold the most cargo are the "best floaters." This investigation enables students to begin to quantify their observations of buoyancy, a new idea that will be reinforced in later lessons.

Materials

For each student
   1   science notebook
   1   lump of clay

For every two students
  30   marbles
   1   plastic tank with 2 liters (2 qt) of water
   1   plastic plate
   1   towel

For the class
   6   sponges
       Several sheets of newsprint

Preparation

1. On a sheet of newsprint, prepare a sample record chart like the one shown in Figure 7-1. In Step 3 of the **Procedure** section, students will be asked to record the number of marbles each boat design will keep afloat.

2. If you need fresh clay, refer to Lesson 3, Step 3 of the **Preparation** section.

3. Arrange for the distribution of water and other materials.

Figure 7-1

Sample record sheet

How Many Marbles Are Kept Afloat?

Boat Design	Number of Marbles

Procedure

1. Ask students to describe the clay boat designs that floated. You may also want to review with the class what they learned about the effect of changing shape on the weight of the clay.

2. Challenge students to use what they have learned about making clay boats to investigate the amount of cargo (number of marbles) that various clay boat designs will keep afloat.

3. Ask students to keep a record in their notebooks of their clay boat designs and of the number of marbles each one kept afloat. Show them the sample record chart you prepared in Step 1 of the **Preparation** section, and ask them to make their own charts in their notebooks.

Figure 7-2

Testing to see how many marbles different boat designs can support

4. In addition, ask students to sketch each boat design they construct and to show the number of marbles it is able to keep afloat. Figure 7-3 shows an example of one student's work.

5. Distribute the materials. Have students work with their partners to test the boat designs that they have constructed.

6. Remind students to record their observations in their notebooks.

Final Activities

1. Ask students to return their materials to the storage area.

2. Discuss with students the various boats they designed and tested. Ask them to identify the designs that held only a few marbles and the designs that held many marbles.

Extensions

SCIENCE

1. Challenge students with the following question: What difference do you think the kind of cargo will make in how well a boat floats? Students can explore this question using equal weights of paper clips, pennies, and marbles. To solve the problem, students can begin by determining the number of paper clips that equal the weight of a marble. They can test their predictions by placing paper clips in each of their boats.

Figure 7-3

*Sample of
student work*

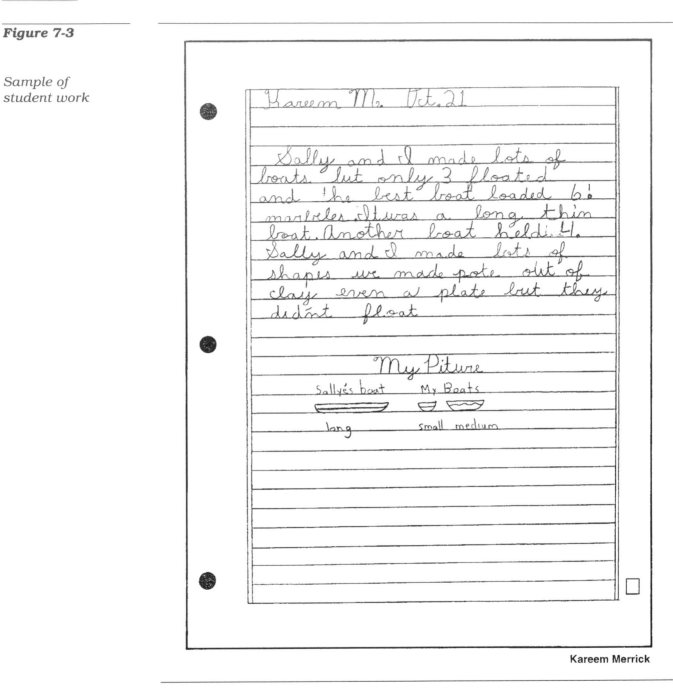

Kareem M. Oct. 21

Sally and I made lots of boats but only 3 floated and the best boat loaded 6½ marbles. It was a long, thin boat. Another boat held 4. Sally and I made lots of shapes we made pots out of clay even a plate but they didn't float

My Piture

Sallye's boat   My Boats

long   small medium

Kareem Merrick

SOCIAL STUDIES

2. Invite students to investigate the variety of designs of cargo boats. Have students create a display for the class. How are all the boat designs similar? How are they different?

Does Size Affect Buoyancy?

Overview and Objectives

In Lesson 7, students investigated how design affects buoyancy. Now they focus on another variable—size—by creating different-sized foil boats that have the same design. Students also feel the upward force of the water and observe how the boats move down in the water as marbles are added. This provides the basis for using a spring scale to investigate this upward force in the next lesson.

- Students discuss the design of clay boats that floated and apply this design to foil boats.

- Students use their sense of touch to explore the buoyant force of the water on the foil boats and relate this to the size of each boat.

- Students predict and test how many marbles each boat will be able to keep afloat.

- Students observe how much of the boat moves below the surface of the water as marbles are added.

- Students discuss and read about boat designs.

Background

The amount of underwater space (volume) that an object occupies is directly related to the phenomenon of buoyancy. Bigger objects **displace,** or move aside, more of the liquid than smaller objects do. It is useful to imagine that the water that has been displaced "pushes up" on the object. This pushing up is called buoyant force. Large boats displace large amounts of liquid, making the buoyant force on them greater than the buoyant force on small boats.

In addition to exploring buoyant force, students also will see many other phenomena that they may want to investigate—water rushing into sinking boats, small pieces of aluminum foil "sticking" to the surface, and bubbles rising from submerged objects. Phenomena such as these are interesting and worth discussing, even though they are not central to this lesson.

Understandably, students' emerging ideas about the buoyant force will not resemble carefully worded scientific explanations. At this point, however, it is more important for students to engage in their own struggle to make sense of what they observe. It is not important that they use all the "right words" to explain their ideas.

Materials

For each student

   1 science notebook
   1 copy of **Record Sheet 8-A: How Many Marbles Can the Boats Hold?**

For every two students

   1 piece of aluminum foil, 10 × 10 cm (4 × 4″)
   1 piece of aluminum foil, 15 × 15 cm (6 × 6″)
   1 piece of aluminum foil, 20 × 20 cm (8 × 8″)
 30 marbles
   1 plastic tank with 2 liters (2 qt) of water
   1 plastic plate
   1 towel

For the class

   6 sponges

Preparation

1. Prepare a set of three aluminum foil squares for each pair of students.

2. Make one copy of **Record Sheet 8-A** for each student.

3. Post the brainstorming list from Lessons 1 and 2. It will be used for the review in Step 1 of the **Procedure** section.

Procedure

1. Ask students to describe which of their clay boat designs floated in Lesson 7. As you have done in previous lessons, use the brainstorming list from Lessons 1 and 2 to review their previous ideas and to add new ideas to the list. You may want to add new ideas with a different-colored pen.

2. Explain to students that in this lesson they will design an aluminum foil boat and that they will construct models of this design in three different sizes. Then they will investigate the effect of size on the number of marbles a boat can keep afloat.

3. Distribute **Record Sheet 8-A** and the three aluminum foil squares to each pair of students.

4. Ask students to work with a partner to construct three different-sized boats of the same design.

5. Distribute the water and marbles.

6. Ask students to place the smallest boat in the water and push down on it gently until it sinks. Challenge students to find words that describe how it felt. (Students might say that they could feel the water pushing up.) Were they surprised? Repeat this with the other two boats. Encourage students to discuss and describe this upward push of the water against the boat.

7. Ask students to use this experience to predict and then test how many marbles each boat will be able to keep afloat. Encourage students to add marbles one at a time and to observe how the boat moves down in the water as they add each marble.

8. Distribute **Record Sheet 8-A.** In the first column, students record the size of the boat and sketch its design. In the second column, students write their predictions of the number of marbles each boat will hold. In the third

Figure 8-1

Constructing boats
from aluminum foil

column, students record the number of marbles each boat did hold. Ask students to draw sketches that show the water line on the boat.

9. Have students return materials to the storage area.

Final Activities

1. Ask students to describe in their notebooks the observations they made as marbles were added to the boats. Then ask them to share their observations. You might want to make a class list.

2. Ask students to read "Boats on the Move." Questions such as the following may help focus their reading:

   ■ What are some of the boats you have seen?

   ■ How are boats used today?

   ■ Why do you think some boats can be so large and heavy and still float?

3. After students have read the selection, invite them to share what they learned about boats that they did not know before.

Extensions

MATHEMATICS

1. Ask students to record the approximate area of the bottom of the large boat. When the boat is holding the maximum number of marbles, have students record the approximate area of the sides of the boat that are under water. Students should then record the total area of the boat that is under water and the total number of marbles the boat kept afloat. Repeat this for the other two boats. Is there a pattern that can be used to predict the number of marbles other boats will keep afloat?

2. Challenge students to design and construct a boat that will keep eight marbles afloat but will sink when a ninth marble is added. This activity could be used as an embedded assessment that will allow you to observe how students tackle this challenge. Look for signs that students understand that changing the size or design of the boat has an effect on the number of marbles it will keep afloat.

Assessment

When you review class discussions and students' products from Lessons 6, 7, and 8, consider the following questions:

- Is the students' knowledge of floating and sinking growing? Were students able to add new ideas to the class lists from Lesson 1? Are students identifying variables that affect the buoyancy of an object?

- Are students becoming aware that the size and design of an object affect the amount of buoyant force pushing upward on it?

- How well are students able to apply what they learned in Lesson 7 about boat design? Do the students' predictions reflect the application of previous experiences?

- Are students becoming aware that a larger boat will hold more marbles?

- Are students becoming aware that buoyant force is pushing upward on the boats?

- How well are students able to explain their ideas and defend the reasoning behind their explanations?

Reading Selection

Boats on the Move

Have you ever been on a boat? It's great fun gliding on the water, feeling the wind blowing through your hair. Boats travel on the ocean and on rivers and lakes. You may have noticed that different kinds of boats travel in different bodies of water.

For example, ferries on the Puget Sound (off the coast of northwestern Washington State) carry thousands of drivers and their automobiles across the water each day. Near tropical islands in the Caribbean Sea, cruise ships serve as "floating hotels," providing vacationers from all over the world with a comfortable base from which to enjoy warm weather.

Some ships and boats have jobs to do. Large ships called icebreakers break ice for smaller ships. Tankers and freighters transport oil, steel, and other cargo across oceans. Submarines dive under water to explore the depths of the sea.

Thousands of years ago, boats carried cargo across bodies of water much as they do today. The early Egyptians built flat, long boats that looked like barges or rafts. One such boat was found buried near the Great Pyramid in Khufu, Egypt.

About one thousand years ago, in what is now Scandinavia, the Vikings designed and built long canoe-shaped ships. These ships could hold 16 oars on each side for speedy paddling, yet they were flat enough on the bottom to maneuver close to shore without running aground.

Early boats and ships were made of wood or bundles of reeds. They were all propelled by the wind or by paddles. But about two hundred years ago, that began to change.

Engineers designed and built ships that relied on steam engines, which had just been invented. In Scotland, an inventor named William Symington built an early steamboat that could move barges. Called the *Charlotte Dundas,* it ran at about three miles an hour.

Over time, ships became more and more sophisticated. For thousands of years, builders had constructed boats from wood. But they began using a more versatile material—metal. Ships made of iron and steel were heavier than wooden ships, but they were larger and could carry more cargo. Today, huge steel ships transport enormous loads of supplies across the oceans of the world.

As you can see, boat designs have changed a lot since the first boats were constructed. But, one early boat—the canoe—is still used today. Thousands of years ago, early Americans paddled similar kinds of boats across the rivers and lakes of North America.

Record Sheet 8-A

Name: _____

Date: _____

How Many Marbles Can the Boats Hold?

Size of Aluminum Foil and Sketch of Boat	Predicted Number of Marbles	Number of Marbles Floated

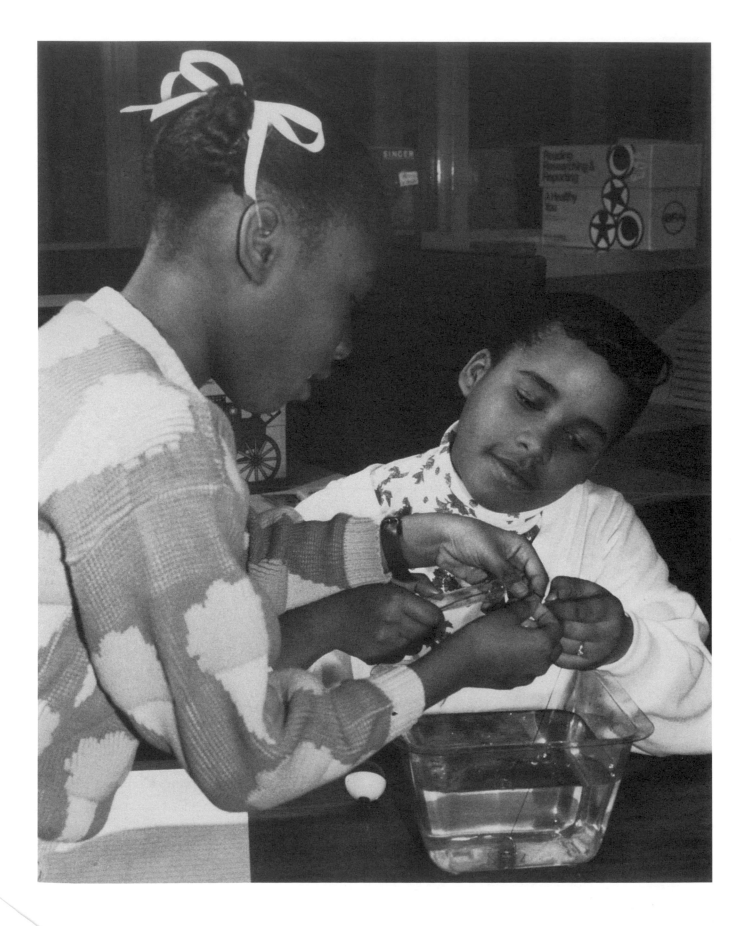

Reading Selection

Boats on the Move

Have you ever been on a boat? It's great fun gliding on the water, feeling the wind blowing through your hair. Boats travel on the ocean and on rivers and lakes. You may have noticed that different kinds of boats travel in different bodies of water.

For example, ferries on the Puget Sound (off the coast of northwestern Washington State) carry thousands of drivers and their automobiles across the water each day. Near tropical islands in the Caribbean Sea, cruise ships serve as "floating hotels," providing vacationers from all over the world with a comfortable base from which to enjoy warm weather.

Some ships and boats have jobs to do. Large ships called icebreakers break ice for smaller ships. Tankers and freighters transport oil, steel, and other cargo across

oceans. Submarines dive under water to explore the depths of the sea.

Thousands of years ago, boats carried cargo across bodies of water much as they do today. The early Egyptians built flat, long boats that looked like barges or rafts. One such boat was found buried near the Great Pyramid in Khufu, Egypt.

About one thousand years ago, in what is now Scandinavia, the Vikings designed and built long canoe-shaped ships. These ships could hold 16 oars on each side for speedy paddling, yet they were flat enough on the bottom to maneuver close to shore without running aground.

Early boats and ships were made of wood or bundles of reeds. They were all propelled by the wind or by paddles. But about two hundred years ago, that began to change.

Engineers designed and built ships that relied on steam engines, which had just been invented. In Scotland, an inventor named William Symington built an early steamboat that could move barges. Called the *Charlotte Dundas,* it ran at about three miles an hour.

Over time, ships became more and more sophisticated. For thousands of years, builders had constructed boats from wood. But they began using a more versatile material—metal. Ships made of iron and steel were heavier than wooden ships, but they were larger and could carry more cargo. Today, huge steel ships transport enormous loads of supplies across the oceans of the world.

As you can see, boat designs have changed a lot since the first boats were constructed. But, one early boat—the canoe—is still used today. Thousands of years ago, early Americans paddled similar kinds of boats across the rivers and lakes of North America.

Record Sheet 8-A

Name: _____

Date: _____

How Many Marbles Can the Boats Hold?

Size of Aluminum Foil and Sketch of Boat	Predicted Number of Marbles	Number of Marbles Floated

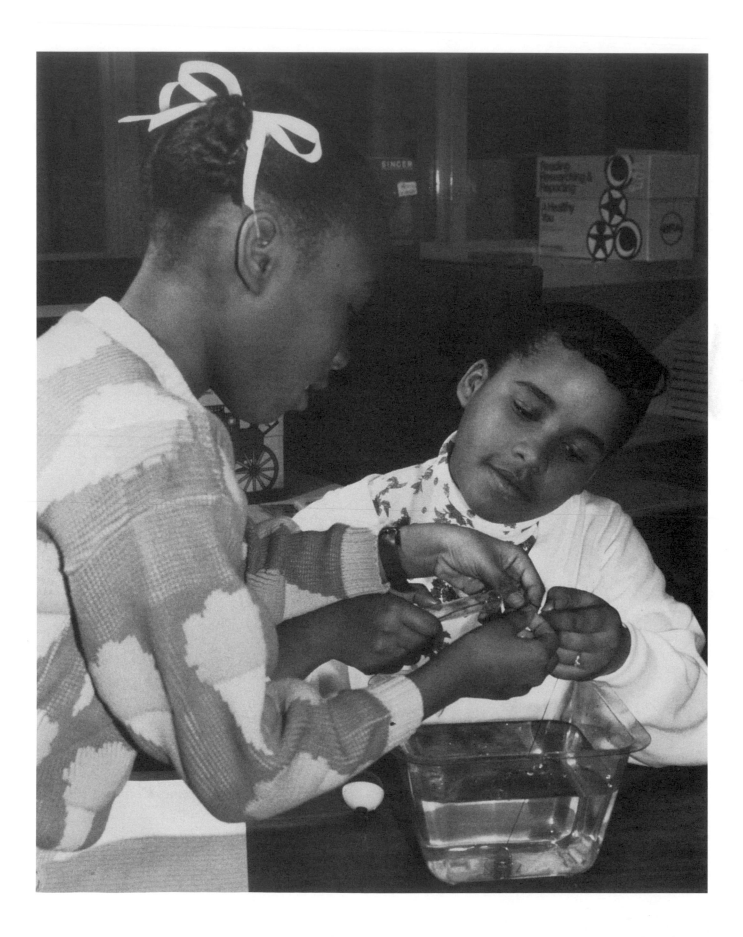

Procedure

1. Review with students what they learned in Lesson 8, when they investigated how many marbles the aluminum foil boats could keep afloat. Ask students to discuss their ideas about the effect that the size of the boat has on how many marbles it will keep afloat.

2. Explain that in this lesson students will have a chance to investigate a floating object—a fishing bobber. First, ask students to estimate the weight of each bobber by holding it in their hands. Then ask them to investigate the buoyant force on each bobber by pushing it under water.

Figure 9-2

Submerging the fishing bobbers

3. Distribute the fishing bobbers and water. Students can begin the activity.

4. After students have had a chance to work with the fishing bobbers, ask them to make two predictions about them. Ask students the following questions:

   - Which fishing bobber do you think weighs the most?

   - Which fishing bobber do you think will have the greatest buoyant force pushing against it?

   Have students put the materials aside for a moment and record their predictions on **Record Sheet 9-A.** Ask them to discuss their ideas with their partners. Remind them to include the reasons for their predictions on Record Sheet 9-A.

5. Distribute the remaining materials. Ask students to weigh each of the fishing bobbers and record the weight on **Record Sheet 9-B.**

6. Ask students to use the directions on pg. 27 in the Student Activity Book to measure the buoyant force on each of the bobbers. These directions can also be found on pg. 84 of the Teacher's Guide.

Final Activities

1. After students finish measuring the buoyant force on each of the bobbers, have them return their materials to the storage area.

2. Ask students to discuss their results. You may want to ask questions such as the following:

   ■ What effect do you think size has on the amount of buoyant force?

   ■ What are some possible reasons that the fishing bobbers float so well?

Extensions

SCIENCE

1. Encourage students to devise ways to measure the buoyant force on other objects. Students may be interested in finding out the buoyant force on clay boats or on the assortment of objects from Lessons 2 and 3.

SOCIAL STUDIES   LANGUAGE ARTS

2. Ask students to write and illustrate an advertisement for fishing bobbers. You may want to ask students to design a special fishing bobber that is needed to catch a very large fish.

Instructions for Preparing a Braided Nylon Cord

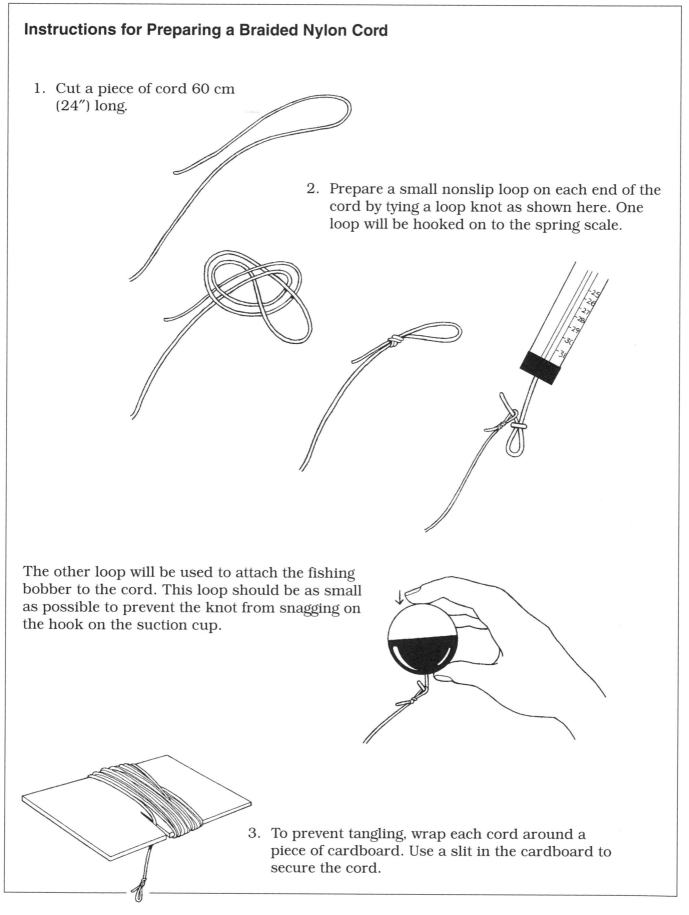

1. Cut a piece of cord 60 cm (24″) long.

2. Prepare a small nonslip loop on each end of the cord by tying a loop knot as shown here. One loop will be hooked on to the spring scale.

The other loop will be used to attach the fishing bobber to the cord. This loop should be as small as possible to prevent the knot from snagging on the hook on the suction cup.

3. To prevent tangling, wrap each cord around a piece of cardboard. Use a slit in the cardboard to secure the cord.

Student Instructions for Measuring the Buoyant Force

1. Thread the string through the hook in the suction cup.

2. Attach one end of the string to the spring scale.

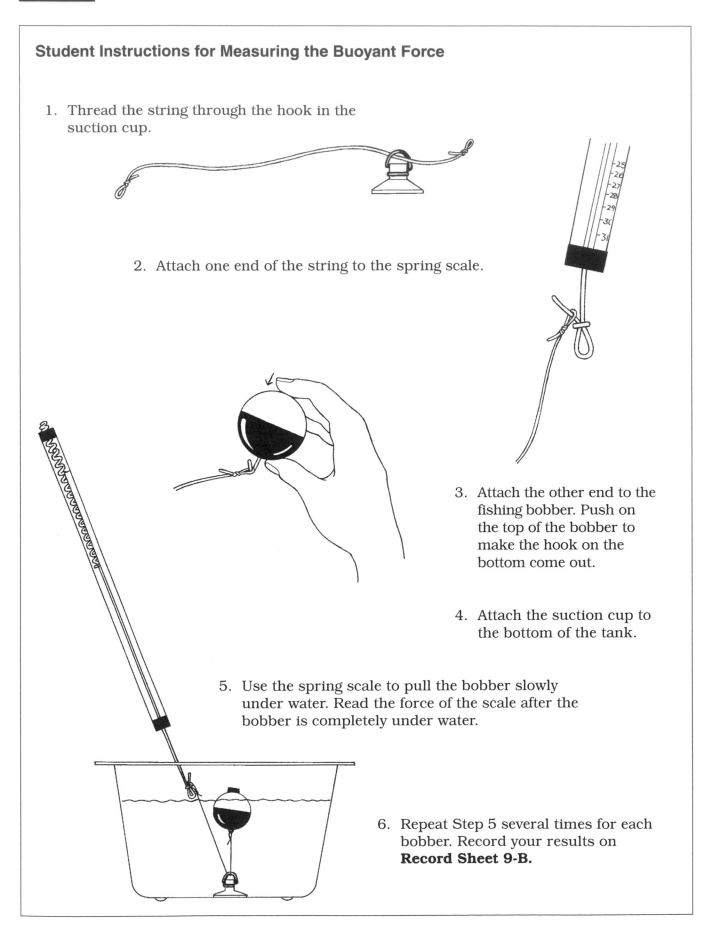

3. Attach the other end to the fishing bobber. Push on the top of the bobber to make the hook on the bottom come out.

4. Attach the suction cup to the bottom of the tank.

5. Use the spring scale to pull the bobber slowly under water. Read the force of the scale after the bobber is completely under water.

6. Repeat Step 5 several times for each bobber. Record your results on **Record Sheet 9-B.**

Record Sheet 9-A

Name: _____

Date: _____

Working with Fishing Bobbers

Prediction: Which fishing bobber do you think weighs the most?

Prediction: Which fishing bobber do you think has the greatest buoyant force?

Reasons: What are some reasons for your predictions?

Use **Record Sheet 9-B** to record the weight of each fishing bobber and the force that it takes to sink each one.

Record Sheet 9-B

Name: _____

Date: _____

Measuring the Forces on the Fishing Bobbers: Weight and Buoyancy

Size of the Fishing Bobber	Weight of the Fishing Bobber	Floating Force of the Fishing Bobbers (in clips)		
		First Measurement	Second Measurement	Third Measurement
Small				
Medium				
Large				

What Happens to the Water?

Overview and Objectives

Having investigated the buoyant force of water on objects, students now observe what happens to the water level when objects are submerged. By submerging objects in a graduated tube and observing that the water level rises, students are introduced to displacement. Continuing this investigation with cylinders that have the same volume but different weights, students learn that displacement is directly related to the volume of the object, not to its weight. The effect of displacement is explored further in the next lesson, where students compare the weight of an object with its weight when measured in water.

- Students calibrate a tube to use as a measuring tool.

- Students observe that water is displaced when objects are placed in it.

- Students measure and record changes in water level caused by holding various objects under water.

- Students compare and discuss water displacement associated with objects that are of the same volume but different weights.

Background

Whenever an object is placed in a liquid, it pushes aside, or **displaces,** the liquid. In a small container, such as a graduated tube, students can easily observe the amount of liquid that has been displaced by the submerged object—the liquid level visibly rises in the container. In large containers, such as a bathtub or sink, the amount of water displaced by the submerged object would be the same as in a small container. The displacement is far more difficult to observe, however, because the water is spread out over a much larger area and the rise in its level is very small.

The large cylinders used in this lesson are the same size, although they have different weights. But because they all have the same volume, they displace the same amount of water when they are held under water. Similarly, the small cylinders all displace a smaller, but equal, amount of water.

Many students will expect the heaviest cylinder to displace the most water because "it pushes the hardest" on the water. Therefore, the discovery that each of the submerged cylinders changes the water level by exactly the same amount despite the weight differences may create a lot of healthy discussion and debate. Students may also observe that the water level rises less—but very slightly less—for the wood cylinder, which floats. This observation may lead to discussion and further exploration of the connection between the amount of the object that is below the surface of the water, displacement, and buoyant force.

Note: In this lesson, students make a clay cylinder that is the same size and shape as the other cylinders. They will test this cylinder with their other objects. The clay cylinders should be saved because they will be used again in Lessons 11, 12, and 14.

Materials

For each student
1 science notebook

For every two students
1 bobby-pin clip (from the spring scale)
1 plastic tube, 4.5×16 cm ($1\frac{3}{4} \times 6''$)
1 ruler, 30 cm
   Large and small cylinders made of aluminum, acrylic, wood, and polyethylene
1 ball of clay, 30 g (1 oz)
1 plastic plate
1 towel
1 piece of masking tape, 15 cm (6″)

For every four students
1 plastic tank with 1 liter (1 qt) of water

For the class
   Newsprint

Preparation

1. Cut one piece of masking tape for each pair of students.

2. Arrange materials for easy distribution. Students will collect the water from the plastic tanks in Step 5 of the **Procedure.**

   Note: The activities in this lesson require less water than was used in previous lessons.

Procedure

1. Ask students to discuss how they might measure how "big" the different-sized fishing bobbers (from Lesson 9) are. Make a list on newsprint of the different strategies they describe. This discussion will help students focus on different ways of knowing "how big" an object is, which will be useful as they investigate the amount of water displaced by submerged objects.

2. Distribute the clay and one each of the small and large cylinders to each pair of students.

3. Ask students to form the lump of clay into large and small cylinders that are the same size and shape as the other cylinders in their collection. Encourage them to discuss with other students how they determined that the clay cylinders were the same size and shape as their other cylinders. Explain that these new cylinders will become part of their collection of objects.

4. After students have had a chance to construct the clay cylinders, distribute the remaining materials.

5. Ask students to calibrate the plastic tube. Show them how to place the masking tape on the plastic tube and use the ruler to mark each centimeter on the tape. Then have students fill the tube with water to the 10-cm mark.

Figure 10-1

Marking centimeters on the tube

6. Ask students to make predictions in their notebooks in response to the following questions: "What do you think will happen to the water level when a large cylinder is lowered into it? How about a small cylinder?"

7. Have students attach a cylinder to the bobby-pin clip and lower it into the water until it is submerged. Ask students to record in their notebooks the water level before and after submerging each object.

8. Allow time for students to explore and discuss other ideas they might have about the displacement of the water.

9. Have students return the materials to the storage area.

Final Activities

1. Ask students what they learned by measuring the change in water level. Questions such as the following may help get the discussion started:

   ■ What are some things that you observed when you held the cylinders under water?

   ■ What were some of the ways your observations surprised you?

   ■ What are some possible reasons you can think of for what you observed?

   Some students may begin to recognize that the magnitude of the rise in water level is directly related to the volume of the object that is under water, not to the object's weight. It is worth spending some time discussing this important concept with the class.

Management Tip: The graduated tubes prepared in this lesson will be used again in Lessons 11 and 15. The clay cylinders will be used again in Lessons 11, 12, and 14.

Figure 10-2

*Observing the rise
in the water level*

2. Ask students to read "Eureka! The Story of Archimedes' Discovery" at the
    end of this lesson on pg. 94 (pg. 32 in the Student Activity Book). From this
    reading selection, they will learn how Archimedes used water displacement
    to solve a mystery.

Extension

[SCIENCE]

Ask students to measure the volume of other objects by submerging them in
water in the graduated tube. Remind them to keep a record of their observations
in their notebooks.

Assessment

As you observe students during Lessons 10, 11, and 12, consider the following
questions.

Performing Experiments

-   How consistent are students' measurements?

-   Do students repeat tests to validate measurements and results?

-   Are students comparing results with each other as a strategy to
    validate them?

Written Work

-   Do students refer to observations when analyzing results?

-   How detailed are students' written observations?

Small-Group and Class Discussions

■ How are students using previous experiences when they make predictions?

■ Are students referring to specific experiences when they share ideas?

■ Do students' descriptions of displacement indicate a growing awareness of the concept?

Eureka! The Story of Archimedes' Discovery

Archimedes lived in Greece more than two thousand years ago. He was a mathematician and inventor who had become famous for many of his ideas. Archimedes was such a talented scientist that he was able to uncover a fraud. Here's how it happened.

A king had given a goldsmith some pure gold and asked him to make a crown. But when the king got the crown back, he heard rumors that the goldsmith may have stolen part of the pure gold and added silver. To keep the king from suspecting anything, the goldsmith made sure that the silver and gold crown weighed as

much as the gold he had been given. Even so, the king knew that something was wrong. He just had no way to prove it.

The king turned to Archimedes for help. He asked Archimedes to think of a way to find out whether the crown was pure gold **without** damaging the crown. Archimedes worked very hard on the problem, but he couldn't come up with a solution.

Then one day when Archimedes was sitting in his bath, he noticed that the water level rose as more and more of his body sank under water. This gave Archimedes an idea about how to find out whether the crown was pure gold. He jumped out of the bath and ran through the town yelling, "Eureka, Eureka," which means "I've got it, I've got it." He was so excited that he forgot to put his clothes on.

Archimedes had thought of an ingenious plan. He knew that gold weighs more than an equal amount of silver, just as aluminum weighs more than an equal amount of clay. He figured that if a silver object, such as a crown, weighed the same as a gold object, the silver object would have to be a little bigger; it would take up more space. He knew that if both objects were lowered one at a time into a bucket of water, the silver object would make the water rise more than the gold. The same would be true if the crown was made of a mixture of gold and silver.

Archimedes weighed the crown by balancing it with bars of pure gold. Then he lowered the pure gold into a bucket of water and marked how high the water rose. If the crown was made of pure gold, it would make the water rise the same amount. However when the crown was lowered into the water, it rose more than the pure gold bars had made it rise. This meant that some silver must have been mixed with the gold to make the crown. It also meant that the goldsmith was guilty of cheating the king and stealing some of the gold.

Archimedes had solved the mystery.

How Much Do Objects Weigh under Water?

Overview and Objectives

This lesson further explores displacement and relates it to buoyant force. In their experiments with clay and aluminum-foil boats and fishing bobbers, students have already observed that there is a greater buoyant force exerted on large objects than on small objects. In Lesson 10, they observed that the water level in the container changes when objects are submerged, displacing some of the water. By weighing objects that are in water, students now discover that because of the buoyant force, objects seem to weigh less when they are submerged. Objects that float appear to weigh nothing at all.

- Students predict and measure the change in apparent weight of objects when they are submerged.

- Students construct a graph that compares the apparent weights of the objects when they are submerged and when they are out of water.

- Students discuss and compare their observations and conclusions.

Background

When an object is submerged in a liquid, it appears to weigh less than it does when it is out of the water. An object's weight, however, remains constant. The weight appears to change in a liquid because the buoyant force of the liquid pushing upward on the object counteracts the downward force of its weight.

When objects that are the same size are lowered into a liquid, they each displace the same amount of liquid. (Students investigated this phenomenon in Lesson 10.) Because an equal amount of liquid is displaced by each of the objects, the buoyant force exerted by the liquid on each of the objects is also the same. This means that each of the objects will appear to lose the same amount of weight when submerged.

Several of the cylinders will float and appear to weigh nothing when in the water. (In order for an object to float, the buoyant force must be equal to or greater than the downward force of gravity.) This observation will lead students to question whether the objects actually weigh nothing, or whether some other explanation might better describe the situation. Encourage students to discuss their explanations with each other at appropriate opportunities, such as Step 1 of the **Final Activities** section.

The activities in this lesson provide students with additional observations about floating and sinking. These observations will be useful to students as they continue to build upon their earlier ideas and experiences.

Materials

For each student

1   science notebook
1   copy of **Record Sheet 11-A: The Weight of Objects**
1   copy of **Record Sheet 11-B: Graphing the Weight of Objects**

For every two students

1   spring scale
1   plastic tank with 2 liters (2 qt) of water
1   collection of large cylinders made of aluminum, acrylic, wood, polyethylene, and clay
1   plastic plate
1   towel

For the class

1   small clay cylinder (from Lesson 10)
35 No. 1 paper clips
    Class graph (from Lesson 5)

Preparation

Make one copy of **Record Sheets 11-A** and **11-B** for each student.

Procedure

1. Ask students to describe what happened to the level of the water when they placed objects in it during Lesson 10. Explain that in this lesson they will investigate what happens to the apparent weight of an object when it is placed in water.

2. Refer to the class graph they made in Lesson 5. Ask students to predict where on the graph they think the clay cylinders belong.

3. Ask several students to weigh a large clay cylinder and a small clay cylinder for the class. Ask several other students to prepare paper clip chains to add to the graph in the appropriate places.

4. Ask students to predict what they think the weight of each of the five large cylinders will be when they are weighed in the water. Ask students to record their predictions in their notebooks. You may want to suggest that they predict whether the cylinders will weigh the same, more, or less than they do when they are suspended in air.

5. Distribute the materials and **Record Sheet 11-A** to each student. Ask students to use the spring scale to measure the apparent weight of each of the five large cylinders in three different situations: suspended in air, partially submerged (half in water), and submerged (below the surface of the water but not on the bottom). Figures 11-2 and 11-3 show what this looks like. Of course, it will not be possible to obtain a submerged weight for objects that float.

    Note: Remind students to fill in the units of measurement (clips) that they are using. A space is provided on Record Sheet 11-A at the top of each column.

6. Ask students to return the materials to the storage area.

Figure 11-1

*Adding the large
and small clay
cylinders to
the graph*

7. Then ask students to use the information they have collected to construct a triple-bar graph on **Record Sheet 11-B** of their measurements of the submerged weights. Remind students to complete the graph with all appropriate labels. A sample graph is shown in Figure 11-4, on pg.101.

Encourage students to discuss their ideas with each other and to record their observations in their notebooks.

Figure 11-2

Weighing an object
that is partially
under water

Figure 11-3

Weighing an object
that is completely
under water

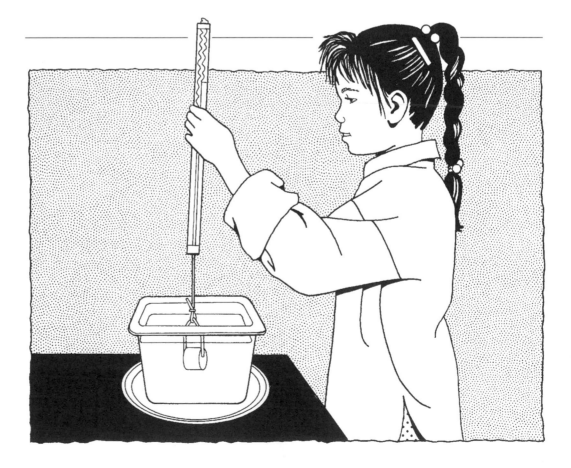

Figure 11-4

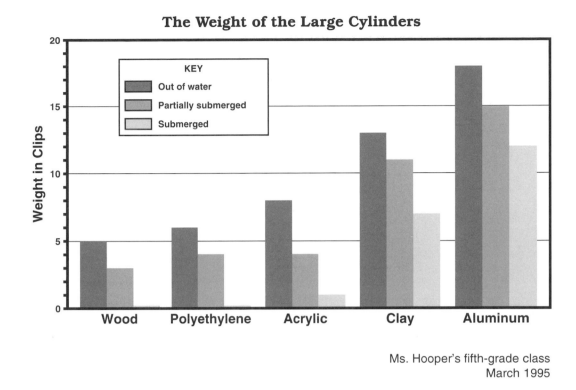

The Weight of the Large Cylinders

KEY
- Out of water
- Partially submerged
- Submerged

Weight in Clips

Wood Polyethylene Acrylic Clay Aluminum

Ms. Hooper's fifth-grade class
March 1995

Final Activity

Discuss with students some of the possible reasons for the phenomena they have observed. Questions such as the following may help get the discussion started:

- Why might the cylinders appear to weigh less under water?

- Why do you think each of the cylinders "loses" about the same amount of weight?

Extensions

SCIENCE

1. Ask students to use the spring scale to weigh other objects that are partially or completely submerged in water. Encourage them to record their observations in their notebooks.

ART

2. If students have gone swimming in shallow water, they may observed that it was much easier to lift something (or someone) in the water than out of it. Ask students to draw a picture that describes this kind of experience.

Record Sheet 11-A

Name: _____

Date: _____

The Weight of Objects

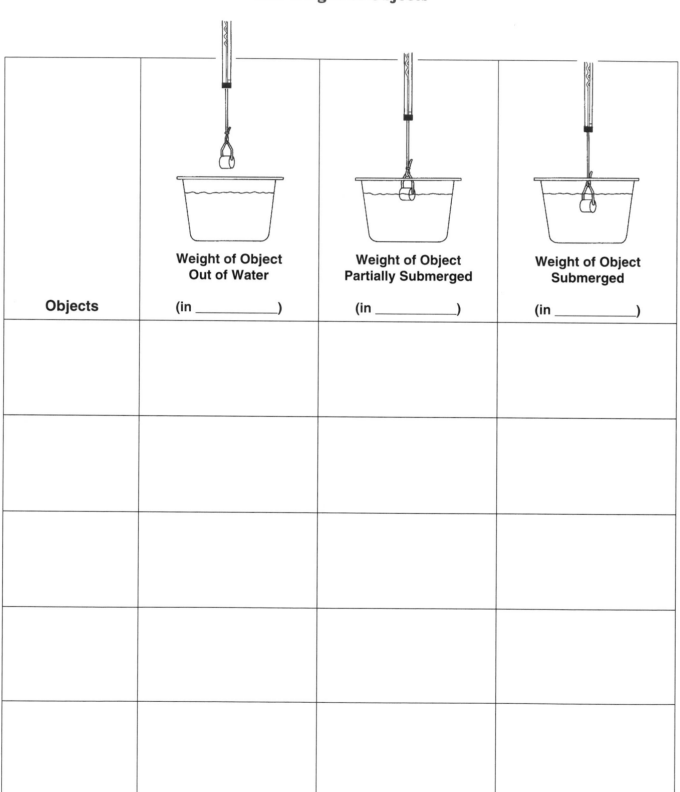

Objects	Weight of Object Out of Water (in _____)	Weight of Object Partially Submerged (in _____)	Weight of Object Submerged (in _____)

Record Sheet 11-B

Name: _____

Date: _____

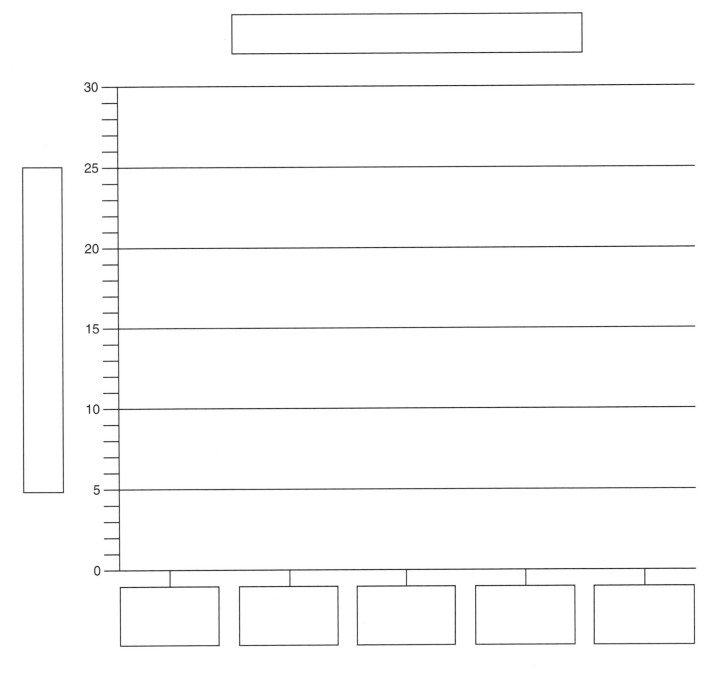

Cylinders

How Much Does Water Weigh?

Overview and Objectives

This lesson provides students with another piece of information to help them determine why some objects float while others sink. By weighing a cylinder of water and comparing it with the weights of solid cylinders that are the same size, students discover the relationship between the weight of water and buoyant force. Objects that weigh more than the same volume of water sink. Objects that weigh less than the same volume of water float. This discovery of the relationship of the liquid to the buoyancy of an object leads students to the investigation of another liquid—salt water—in the next three lessons.

- Students weigh a cylinder of water with a spring scale.

- Students graph the weight of the cylinder of water on the class graph.

- Students compare the weight of the water with the weight of the other cylinders.

- Students construct individual graphs to represent the weights of the solid cylinders and water.

- Students discuss the relationship between the weight of water and the phenomena of floating and sinking.

Background

The weight of a liquid—such as water—is more difficult to measure than the weight of a solid. A liquid must be contained somehow, and a specific amount of liquid must be measured out. In addition, the weight of the container must be considered. Galileo Galilei, who investigated the weights of liquids and solids in the late 1500s and early 1600s, called the weight of a specified amount of liquid the **specific weight** of the liquid. The idea of weighing equal, specific amounts of materials is useful for making comparisons and predictions. In fact, this concept is the essence of the investigation that students conduct in this lesson. They weigh an amount of water equal in volume to the large solid cylinders so that they can compare the weights.

Materials

For each student
1   science notebook
1   copy of **Record Sheet 12-A: The Weight of Water and Other Materials**

Materials

For every two students
1   spring scale
1   plastic cylindrical container, 2.5 × 2.5 cm (1 × 1″)
1   collection of large cylinders made of aluminum, acrylic, wood, polyethylene, and clay
1   plastic plate
1   towel
1   piece of masking tape, 10 cm (4″)

For every four students
1   plastic tank with 1 liter (1 qt) of water

For the class
2   equal-arm balances
30   No. 1 paper clips
Class graph (from Lessons 5 and 11)

Preparation

1.   Prepare a piece of masking tape as a "handle" for each plastic cylindrical container. Fold the masking tape lengthwise against itself in the middle, but leave it sticky on the ends to attach it to the container. You may want to ask students to help with this task.

Figure 12-1

Preparing masking tape handles

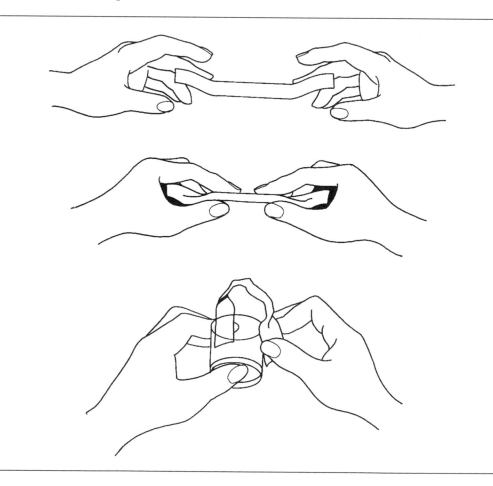

2. Make one copy of **Record Sheet 12-A** for each student.

3. Arrange for the distribution of water and the other materials.

4. Remove the bobby-pin clip from the spring scale.

Management Tip: Caution students not to place the large solid cylinders completely inside the plastic cylindrical containers. While it is valuable for students to see that the cylinders are the same size as the containers, the fit is very snug. It is difficult to remove a cylinder once it is stuck.

Procedure

1. Ask students to review the class weight graph that they helped construct in Lessons 5 and 11. Line up the large cylinders from lightest to heaviest and ask students to discuss the ways the cylinders are alike and different. Figure 12-2 shows a few likely student responses.

Figure 12-2

Comparing the Cylinders

Ways the Cylinders Are Alike	Ways the Cylinders Are Different
size shape amount solid	color weight softness material feel

2. Introduce today's activity by asking students to discuss the following questions before investigating:

   ■ If we want to compare the weight of a solid cylinder with the weight of water, how much water should we use?

   ■ How could you measure the weight of the water?

   ■ Do you think the weight of the container will affect the measurement of the water's weight? How?

3. Ask students to make predictions about where water will fit on the class graph. Remind students to record their predictions in their notebooks along with their reasons.

4. Distribute the materials. Ask students to use the spring scale to measure the weight of the cylinder of water. Encourage them to repeat their measurements at least three times and to compare their results with those of other students. Ask students to record their measurements in their notebooks.

   Note: In Step 4 of the **Preparation** section, it is suggested that you remove the bobby-pin clip for this activity. By suspending the cylindrical container and masking tape handle directly from the spring scale, you can compare the weight of the water directly with the weight of the solid cylinders. If you leave the bobby-pin clip on, an additional weight of almost one paper clip will be introduced. (The cylindrical container also weighs about one paper clip, so in effect you are substituting the container for the bobby pin. If you keep the bobby-pin clip on, then its weight will have to be subtracted.)

5. Ask students to use their data to try to decide where to place water on the class graph. They may want to use the spring scale to verify the weights of some of the solid objects to determine where to place water in the sequence.

Figure 12-3

Weighing a cylinder of water

Final Activities

1. Make room on the class graph to place water where students believe it belongs. Use a chain of paper clips to indicate the weight of the water.

2. Review with students the class weight graph that they have constructed. Ask students to discuss how they think the weight of the cylinder of water could be used to predict whether the solid cylinders will float or sink.

3. Have students use the information from the class graph to construct a graph on **Record Sheet 12-A.** Remind them to complete the graph with all the appropriate labels. A sample graph is shown in Figure 12-4. As students construct their graphs, encourage them to use an equal-arm balance to compare the weight of the water directly with the weight of the other cylinders.

4. Now ask students to refer to their data to investigate the relationship between the weight of the cylinders and their buoyancy.

At this point, some of your students may begin to recognize that the sinking cylinders weigh more than the cylinder of water, while the floating cylinders weigh less. They will have opportunities to investigate this further in Lessons 14 and 16.

Figure 12-4

Sample graph

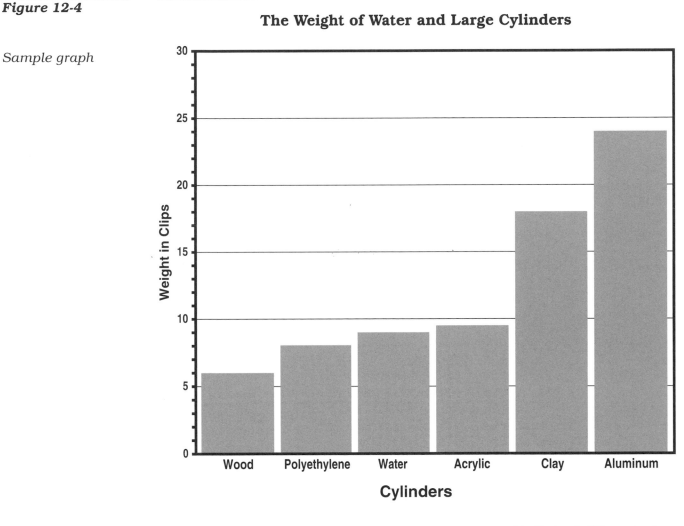

The Weight of Water and Large Cylinders

Mr. Hartney's fifth-grade class
October 1994

Extensions

SCIENCE   MATHEMATICS

1. Challenge students to weigh equal amounts of other liquids, such as milk, soft drinks, oil, and shampoo. Then they can construct a graph of their observations. Encourage students to present their findings to the class.

> **Safety Tip**
>
> Caution students not to experiment with liquids that are highly corrosive, toxic, or flammable.

SCIENCE

2. Ask students to freeze a cylinder of water and to measure the weight of ice. Ask them to compare the weight of the ice with the original weight of the water in the cylinder. Students may discover that although water expands, or increases in volume, when it freezes, it weighs the same whether it is liquid or frozen. Because ice has a greater volume than liquid water, it displaces more liquid and has a greater buoyant force. It therefore floats.

SCIENCE

3. Ask students to predict and test whether various canned soft drinks and juices (of the same size) will float or sink. Encourage students to develop their ideas about why a particular can floated or sank. (For example, do all diet soft drinks float, or just the ones that don't have caffeine?)

Record Sheet 12-A

Name: _____

Date: _____

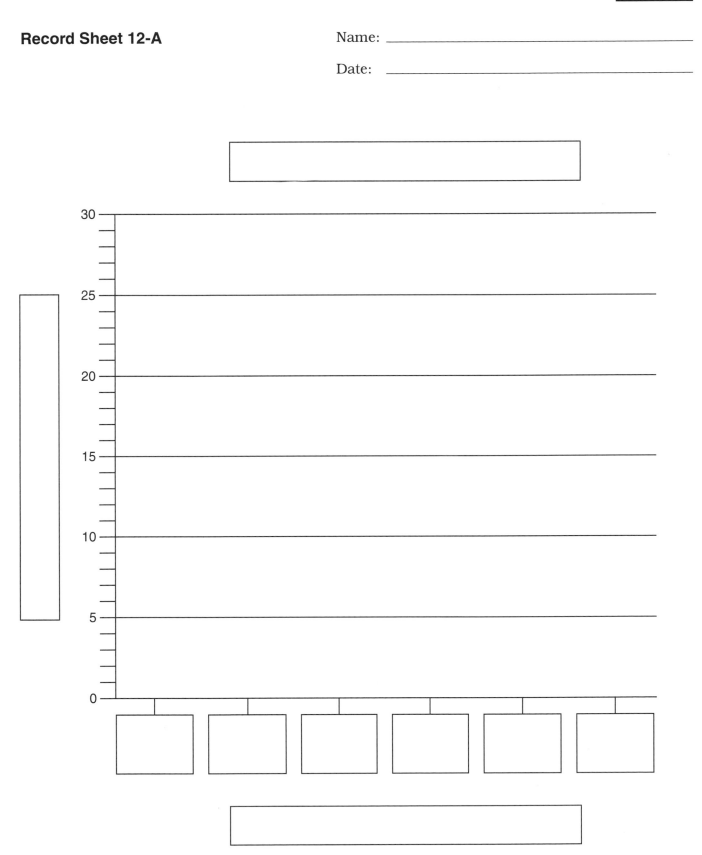

Dissolving Salt in Water

Overview and Objectives

In the next three lessons, students work with salt water to investigate the effect that a heavier liquid has on an object's buoyancy. During the first part of this lesson, students are introduced to salt water as a solution. They observe how various amounts of salt interact with and dissolve in a drop of water. During the second part of the lesson, students discover that salt water is heavier than fresh water. In the next lesson, students apply this information to predict whether objects will float or sink in salt water.

- Students predict what will happen when they mix salt and water.

- Students test their predictions.

- Students observe and describe the changes that occur in salt and water when the two are mixed.

- Students observe and describe the changes in salt water over time.

- Students compare the weight of salt water with the weight of fresh water.

- Students form hypotheses that explain their results.

Background

Adding salt to water forms a saltwater solution as the salt dissolves in the water. After a certain amount of salt has been added, however, the salt will no longer dissolve in the water; it will remain solid. At this point, the salt and water solution has become what is called a **saturated** solution.

In this lesson, students are asked to make predictions about how salt will interact with the water. Students who have worked on the unit have made predictions such as the following:

- "The salt will make the water thicker."

- "The salt will make the water heavier."

- "The salt will disappear, dissolve, or evaporate."

- "The salt will make the water overflow."

As students watch the interaction of salt and water, they will be excited about what they observe and may develop theories to explain their observations. Effective questioning on your part will encourage students to pursue their theories and investigate them on their own. Asking open-ended questions, such as those listed below, may help students focus on ways to make sense of their observations. Asking such questions at opportune times during the lesson may encourage students to come up with their own questions as well.

■ How many salt grains (or flakes) will dissolve in one drop of water?

■ What do you think will happen to the salt water if you let it sit uncovered overnight? What would happen if you covered it?

■ How do you think the weight of salt water will compare with the weight of water?

In the second half of the lesson, students will weigh water, salt, and salt water and discover that salt water weighs more than fresh water. In Lessons 14 and 15, students will explore how the weight of the liquid affects buoyancy. Students also might note no change in the volume of the water as the salt dissolves.

Note: This lesson will probably take longer than other lessons, but it can easily be divided into two sessions. You may find that students become engaged in a wide variety of investigations of their own, in addition to exploring the suggested activities.

Materials

For each student

  1 science notebook
  1 flat wooden toothpick
  1 piece of waxed paper, 10 cm (4″) square
  1 small plastic spoon
  1 copy of **Record Sheet 13-A: Weighing Salt, Water, and Salt Water**

For every two students

  1 spring scale
  1 plastic cylindrical container with masking tape handle (from Lesson 12)
  1 plastic dropper
  2 plastic cups and lids, 300 ml (10 oz)
  1 plastic teaspoon
  1 plastic plate
  1 towel

For every four students

  1 plastic tank with 2 liters (2 qt) of water

For the class

  2 boxes of kosher salt, flaked, 1.5 kg (3 lb)
     Masking tape

Preparation

1. Duplicate one copy of **Record Sheet 13-A** for each student.

2. Fill the plastic tanks with water for each team of four students.

3. Cut one piece of waxed paper for each student.

4. Pour salt into 15 plastic cups so that each is about one-quarter full. Cover the cups with lids.

5. Stick a piece of masking tape on the handle of each small spoon.

    Note: Store salt in a sealed container so that it will not absorb water from the air. Placing a few rice grains in the container of salt will help.

Procedure

1. Ask students what they think will happen when they mix salt and water. Have them record their predictions in their notebooks.

2. Have students begin the investigation by mixing salt and water. The instructions on pg. 44 of the Student Activity Book give them the guidance they need. For your information, these directions are included on pg. 117 of the Teacher's Guide.

> **Safety Tip**
>
> Concentrated salt water can sting if it contacts cuts or sensitive skin, and it will dehydrate skin after prolonged contact. So encourage students to rinse their hands with fresh water after working with salt water.

3. Distribute the waxed paper, droppers, toothpicks, and salt. Encourage students to discuss what they are doing with other members of their team. Remind them to use their notebooks to record their observations.

4. To prepare for an overnight investigation of salt water, ask students to write their names on the tape on the small spoon. Ask students to put one small drop of salt water on the spoon. Have students move the spoons to an out-of-the-way place, such as a window ledge, where they will not be disturbed.

5. Ask students to record a prediction in their notebooks about the drop of salt water. Ask them, "What do you think will happen to the salt water if you let it sit out overnight?"

Figure 13-1

Putting salt water on a spoon

6. Now ask students to make another prediction, this time on **Record Sheet 13-A.** Ask them how they think the weight of each of the following will compare: a cylindrical container of salt, a cylindrical container of salt water, and a cylindrical container of water, which they weighed in Lesson 12. Suggest that they predict the order of the weights from lightest to heaviest.

Management Tip: During the lesson, students pour out and mix salt and water. To minimize the mess produced by these activities, it is a good idea to discuss ahead of time strategies for successful pouring, measuring, and mixing. Suggestions such as the following may be helpful:

■ Use a dry cylindrical container to weigh salt and a wet cylindrical container to weigh water or salt water.

■ Pour carefully or use a spoon to transfer small amounts.

■ To contain spills, do all pouring, measuring, and mixing over a plastic plate.

7. Distribute the remaining materials. Ask students to work with a partner to weigh cylindrical containers of salt, water, and salt water. Directions for doing this are on pgs. 45–46 of the Student Activity Book. For your information, the directions are included on pgs. 118–119 of the Teacher's Guide.

Final Activities

1. Ask students to return the materials to the storage area.

2. Ask students to compare with other students what they have observed. Have them share their ideas about possible reasons for differences in their measurements. You may want to make a list of students' ideas. Questions such as the following may help focus the discussion:

■ What were some of the things you observed while you were mixing and measuring?

■ What are some possible reasons for the differences in measurements?

Extensions

SCIENCE

1. Encourage students to investigate how many salt grains will dissolve in one or two drops of water. Then ask them to predict how many salt grains will dissolve in three or four drops of water. Suggest that they test their predictions.

SCIENCE

2. Ask students to try mixing other materials with water to find out which materials dissolve and which materials do not. Encourage them to devise additional investigations and to write about what they do.

Safety Tip

Tell students to ask an adult to help them select materials to test. Toxic materials should be avoided.

Student Instructions for Mixing Salt with Water

1. Place one or two drops of water on the waxed paper.

2. Place three or four salt grains on the waxed paper near the water.

3. Use a toothpick to move the water drop around and to mix the salt and water. What are some things that you observe happening?

4. Record your observations in your notebook.

5. What are some other investigations of salt and water that you would like to try to do? Write your questions in your notebook and then investigate on your own or with a partner. Here are a few suggestions:

   ■ What will happen if you use more salt?

   ■ What if you use less water?

Student Instructions for Comparing Weights of Salt, Water, and Salt Water

Weighing Salt

1. Make sure the small cylindrical container is dry. Carefully fill it to the top with salt. Brush the top with your finger to make sure the top is level.

2. Test your prediction by weighing the small container of salt with the spring scale. Remember to record the weight in your notebook.

3. Pour the small container of salt into an empty cup.

Weighing Water

4. Fill the small container with water as close to the top as possible.

5. Use the spring scale to weigh the water, as you did in Lesson 12. Record the weight in your science notebook.

Mixing Salt Water

6. Add the small container of water to the salt you poured into the cup in Step 3. Stir the mixture. What are some things you observe?

Weighing Salt Water

7. Pour the remaining dry salt into the cup containing the salt and water. Add enough fresh water to make a cupful of salt water. Stir the mixture. What are some things you now observe?

8. After you have stirred the salt water for several minutes, fill the small container with salt water as close to the top as possible.

9. Weigh the salt water with the spring scale. Record the weight in your notebook. Pour the water back into the cup.

10. Write your observations of the weights of salt, water, and salt water on **Record Sheet 13-A.**

11. Compare your observations with your predictions. Discuss them with your partner. What are some things you discovered?

12. Put a lid on your cup of salt water and set it aside. You will use it again in Lesson 14 to test whether objects float or sink.

Record Sheet 13-A

Name: _____

Date: _____

Weighing Salt, Water, and Salt Water

Predict the weights of salt, water, and salt water from the lightest to heaviest.

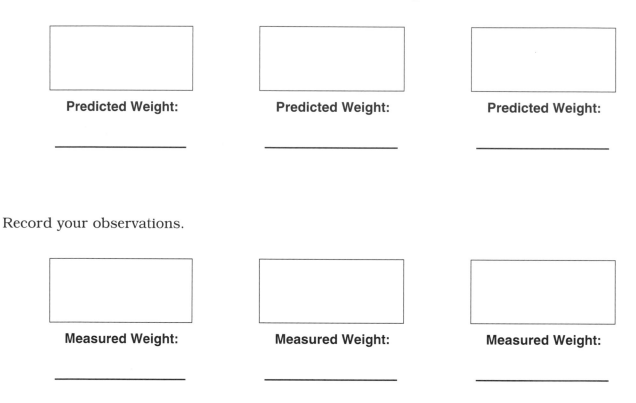

Predicted Weight: **Predicted Weight:**   **Predicted Weight:**

_____   _____   _____

Record your observations.

Measured Weight: **Measured Weight:**   **Measured Weight:**

_____   _____   _____

Compare your observations with your predictions.

Discuss them with your partner.

What are some things you discovered?

How Is Salt Water Different from Fresh Water?

Overview and Objectives

Students continue exploring the differences between fresh and salt water by returning to the collection of objects from Lesson 3. After testing each of the objects in salt water, students discover that salt water exerts a greater buoyant force than fresh water does. The increased buoyant force is caused by the added weight of the salt. This concept becomes particularly clear as students discover that some objects that sink in fresh water will float in salt water.

■ Students predict which objects will float in salt water.

■ Students test their predictions and record their results.

■ Students apply information about the weight of salt water to make predictions about whether a variety of objects will float or sink in salt water.

■ Students add the weight of the salt water to the class graph.

■ Students discuss why objects that sink in fresh water can float in salt water.

Background

It probably came as no surprise to students in Lesson 13 that salt water is heavier than fresh water. More accurately, salt water is denser than fresh water because of the weight of the dissolved salt. This greater density of salt water, as compared with fresh water, increases the buoyancy of objects. People who swim in very salty bodies of water, such as the Great Salt Lake in Utah, notice that it takes very little effort to float.

Liquids with a greater density than fresh water push up on objects with a greater buoyant force. In this lesson, the buoyant force of salt water is great enough to cause both acrylic cylinders and the nylon bolt to float, even though they sink in fresh water.

However, the concentration of salt needs to be very high in order for the acrylic cylinders to float. If some of your students find that the acrylic cylinders sink, you may want to take advantage of this opportunity to discuss with the class the possible reasons for the discrepancy and to suggest that students investigate the effect of adding more salt. Students also may wish to investigate the effect of adding more water, which will dilute the concentration of salt.

Figure 14-1

Swimmers in Great Salt Lake

Materials

For each student

  1 science notebook

  1 copy of completed **Record Sheet 12-A: The Weight of Water and Cylinders** (from Lesson 12)

For every two students

  1 covered plastic cup of salt water, 300 ml (10 oz)

  1 set of objects (from Lesson 3)

  1 plastic teaspoon

  1 plastic plate

  1 towel

For the class

    Small spoons with evaporated salt water (from Lesson 13)

  35 No. 1 paper clips

    Class graph (from Lesson 12)

Preparation

1. Check to see whether the salt water set aside in the small spoons has evaporated enough for the salt crystals to be visible.

2. Check the resealable bags of objects used in Lesson 3 to make sure that each contains all the objects students will need for their experiments.

Procedure

1. Distribute the spoons (from Lesson 13) in which students set aside a drop of salt water. Ask students to discuss with their partners what they observe. Then ask students to record their observations in their notebooks. Questions such as the following may help students focus their observations:

   ■ What are some ways that the material in the spoon is different now than at the end of Lesson 13?

   ■ How do you think these changes occurred?

   ■ How could you test to see whether the salt left after the water evaporates weighs the same as the salt that was dissolved to make salt water?

   Note: As an interesting "side investigation," prepare an extra cup of salt water using the directions in Lesson 13. Leave the salt water uncovered for several weeks. After the water has evaporated, ask the class to weigh the remaining salt and compare the weight with that of the salt used to prepare the salt water. This experience will help students understand that the salt remains in the water after it dissolves and that the weight of the salt makes salt water heavier than fresh water.

2. Explain to students that in this lesson they will again predict, as they did in Lesson 3, whether a set of objects will float or sink. Ask students to look in their notebooks and review the predictions and observations they made on **Record Sheet 3-A: Prediction Record.**

3. Now ask students to predict whether the various objects will float or sink in salt water. Remind them to write their predictions and their reasons in their notebooks. Encourage students to organize their predictions into a table.

4. Distribute the materials. Ask students to test their predictions by gently placing the objects one at a time in the cup of salt water. Encourage them to discuss their observations with other students and to record them in their notebooks.

Figure 14-2

Objects floating in salt water

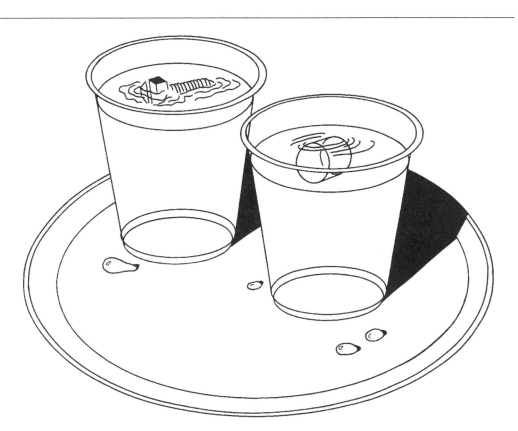

Final Activities

1. Ask students to return their materials to the storage area and clean up their work area. Save the salt water by placing the lids on the cups. The salt water will be used again in Lessons 15 and 16.

2. Discuss with students what they discovered by testing their predictions. Encourage them to describe possible reasons for what they observed, particularly about the floating acrylic cylinders and the nylon bolt, both of which sank in fresh water. What are some new questions raised by these observations? How might they seek answers to these questions?

   For many students, the process of expressing their ideas will be productive, because it will help them build connections between what they have observed in this lesson and their experiences in other lessons.

3. Make room on the class graph to place the weight of the cylinder of salt water where it belongs. Add a chain of paper clips to indicate the weight of the salt water.

   Note: The acrylic cylinder is slightly lighter than an equal amount of saturated salt water, but some students probably will find the weights equal.

   Have students review the graph they made in Lesson 12 (**Record Sheet 12-A**). Ask students to look at the graph for clues that could help them predict whether an object will float or sink. Explain that they will have a chance to make and test predictions about mystery objects in Lesson 16.

   Note: This is an excellent opportunity to encourage students to look for additional evidence to determine which material is heavier. For example, you may suggest that students use the equal-arm balance to weigh the materials. In addition, some students may notice that the weight of the large acrylic cylinder is between the weights of the fresh water and salt water. This is an important observation in developing an understanding of why acrylic floats in salt water but sinks in fresh water.

Extensions

MATHEMATICS

1. Challenge students to use their math skills to answer questions about the saltwater mixture they have created. Ask them to solve problems such as the following, and encourage them to devise and exchange questions of their own. Students can use the equal-arm balance to test their predictions.

   ■ How much do you think the salt in the salt water weighs? What makes you think so?

   ■ If you mixed eight containers of water with two containers of salt, how much do you think the salt water would weigh?

LANGUAGE ARTS

2. Ask students to write and illustrate a story about a real sea creature who takes an imaginary journey from the salty ocean to visit a freshwater river or lake. Encourage students to find out as much as they can about the creature they choose before writing their stories.

Constructing a Hydrometer

Overview and Objectives

To further investigate how the buoyancy of objects is affected by fresh and salt water, students construct a device that can be used to determine how heavy a liquid is compared with fresh water. This tool is called a hydrometer. From their observations and discussions of the levels at which the hydrometer floats in salt water and fresh water, students develop explanations for the observed differences. This information is applied in the last lesson, where students have the opportunity to further test their ideas about the two liquids.

- Students construct a hydrometer.

- Students make predictions about how high the hydrometer will float in salt water.

- Students use a hydrometer to compare salt water and fresh water.

- Students extend their ideas about hydrometers through reading and discussion.

Background

A **hydrometer** is a tool that can be used to compare the densities or relative weights of equal volumes of different liquids. A hydrometer is usually clearly marked to indicate the point at which it floats in fresh water.

In this lesson, students construct a hydrometer by sealing the end of a plastic straw with a ball of clay. To calibrate the hydrometer in fresh water, students must first manipulate the straw and clay so that a mark on the straw is level with the liquid in the cylinder (see Figure 15-1). Students can do this by adding or removing clay from the straw, adding water to the straw, or making a new mark on the straw.

By measuring how high a hydrometer floats in a liquid other than water, an observer can tell immediately if the liquid is heavier or lighter than water. For example, a hydrometer floats higher in salt water than it does in fresh water, indicating that salt water is heavier than fresh water.

Hydrometers are used in a number of different ways. One application is in testing the coolant in car radiators. The level at which the hydrometer floats indicates the concentration of antifreeze in the radiator fluid. The more antifreeze there is in the mixture, the higher the hydrometer will float. This is because the antifreeze is heavier than the water it is mixed with.

Another use for hydrometers is in brewing beer. Brewers use a hydrometer to determine the alcohol content of beer as it ferments. Since alcohol weighs less than water, the hydrometer floats lower when there is a high alcohol concentration than it does when there is less alcohol. Hydrometers also are used to determine the "saltiness," or **salinity,** of water.

After constructing hydrometers in this lesson, students make predictions about how high their hydrometers will float in salt water. Then they test their predictions. It is important for students to have an opportunity to discuss the reasons for their predictions before testing them. The process of making and testing predictions and recording and discussing ideas helps students build a better conceptual understanding of buoyancy and apply this knowledge in new contexts.

Figure 15-1

A hydrometer floating in water

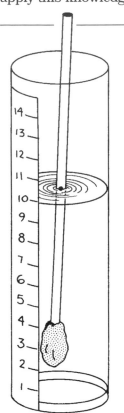

Materials

For each student

  1 science notebook

For every two students

  2 small plastic straws, 4 mm (³⁄₁₆″) in diameter and 14 cm (5½″) long
  1 lump of clay, 15 g (½ oz)
  1 graduated cylinder (from Lesson 10)
  1 plastic teaspoon
  1 plastic plate
  1 towel

For every four students

  1 plastic tank with 1 liter (1 qt) of water
  1 cup of salt water (from Lesson 14)

For the class

  1 permanent marker

Preparation

1. Use a permanent marker to make a mark in the middle of each of the plastic straws. One way to do this quickly is shown in Figure 15-2.

Figure 15-2

Marking the straws

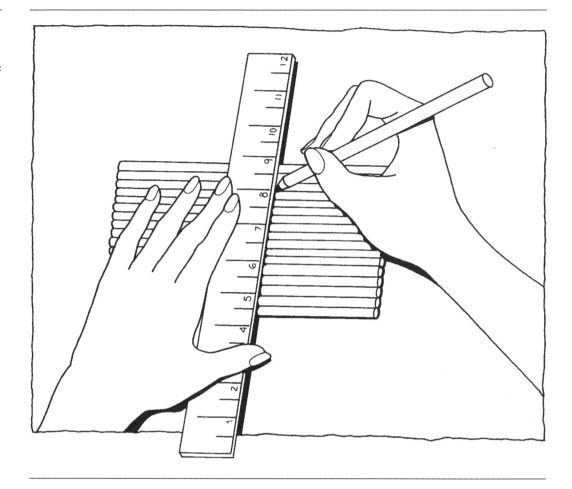

2. Prepare a small lump of clay about the size of a marble for each pair of students to use in constructing their hydrometers.

3. Arrange materials for easy distribution. Students will collect the water from the plastic tanks in Step 3 of the **Procedure.**

Procedure

1. Review with students the observations they made in Lesson 14 as part of their investigation of salt water. Questions such as the following may help remind students of what they experienced in the last lesson:

   ■ What were some things you discovered by making and testing your predictions about salt water?

   ■ How do you think you would explain some of your observations?

2. Show students the graduated cylinder, clay, and straw that they will be working with. Explain that they will be using these materials to construct their own hydrometers. Figure 15-3 shows a student constructing a hydrometer.

3. Distribute the water, graduated cylinder, straws, and clay to the students. Ask students to fill their graduated cylinder to the 10-cm level with fresh water. Challenge them to make the straw and clay float so that the mark on the straw is even with the water level.

Figure 15-3

*Constructing a
hydrometer*

4. Encourage students to discuss among themselves the strategies they might use to change the way the hydrometer floats so that the mark is at the surface of the water. Some may try adding water inside the straw, while others may try adding or removing clay. Tell the student not to change their hydrometers after getting them to float at the freshwater mark.

5. Ask students to set their materials aside for a moment so that they can write in their notebooks. Ask them to record a prediction about how they think their hydrometers will float in salt water. Encourage them to include sketches of what they think will happen, along with their reasons for the predictions.

6. After students have completed their predictions, ask them to test them by placing their hydrometers in salt water. Have two pairs of students work together as a team of four. Ask one pair to pour the fresh water out of their graduated cylinder into the plastic tank and replace it with salt water. This will allow students to compare the salt water directly with the fresh water, as shown in Figure 15-4.

7. Remind students to record their observations in their notebook. Questions such as the following may help students focus their observations:

    ■ What are some possible reasons that the hydrometer floats higher in the salt water?

    ■ Is there a relationship between how much higher the hydrometer floats and the weight of the salt? Can you design an experiment to test your ideas?

Figure 15-4

The hydrometer floats higher in salt water than in fresh water

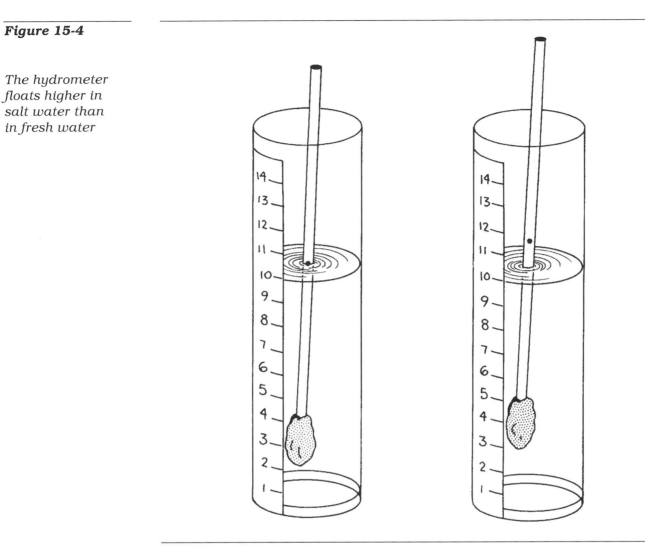

Final Activities

1. Ask students to return the materials to the storage area. Be sure to save the salt water for use in Lesson 16.

2. Ask students to describe what they observed in their investigation of hydrometers. As part of the class discussion, ask students to share their ideas about how a hydrometer works and what it might be used for.

3. Ask students to read "The Story of the Plimsoll Mark," on pg. 52 in the Student Activity Book and pg. 135 in the Teacher's Guide. Questions such as the following may help make the reading productive for students:

   ■ What are some reasons for putting a Plimsoll mark on the side of a ship?

   ■ How do you think the Plimsoll mark got its name?

   ■ What are some ways that a ship with a Plimsoll mark is like the straw you investigated in this lesson?

Extensions

SCIENCE

1. Ask students to test a variety of liquids with their hydrometers. Encourage students to make predictions and discuss the reasons for their predictions before testing them. Finally, remind students to write about their observations.

    Note: Cooking oil is an interesting liquid to test with a hydrometer because it is lighter than an equal amount of water, despite its "thickness," or **viscosity.** (The hydrometer will float lower in this oil than it does in water.) Working with cooking oil, however, is messy. If you decide to use oil, clean up with dish detergent and a brush. To avoid extensive cleanup, you may wish to conduct a class demonstration only.

SCIENCE

2. Encourge students to investigate how high the hydrometer floats in different saltwater mixtures.

> **Safety Tip**
>
> Some liquids that students may wish to test may be hazardous in some way. Be sure to determine whether a particular liquid is harmful before permitting its use in the classroom.

Assessment

In Lessons 13, 14, and 15, students have made and tested a number of predictions about salt water. They have measured the weight of a cylinder of salt water and compared it with the weight of a cylinder of fresh water. They also have discussed how objects float in salt water and in fresh water. And in Lesson 15, they constructed a tool with which to compare the relative weight of liquids.

Students have recorded many of their predictions, ideas, and observations in their notebooks. What they have written and drawn provides you with evidence of their learning. As you review their work from Lessons 13, 14, and 15, consider the following questions:

- What are students' observations about salt dissolving in water to form salt water? Do their observations show an understanding that salt water is a mixture of these two materials?

- Have students recorded their predictions? Is there evidence that they have tested their predictions?

- Do students' predictions and observations about the comparative weights of fresh water and salt water demonstrate an awareness that salt water weighs more than fresh water?

- What are students' predictions and observations about how a hydrometer will float in salt water?

- Do students' entries in their notebooks reflect their ability to test predictions?

Lesson 16 also is an excellent opportunity to assess what students have accomplished. The activities provide students with a chance to use and apply many of the skills and ideas they have been developing over the course of the unit.

Reading Selection

The Story of the Plimsoll Mark

You probably noticed that the hydrometer that you made floated higher in salt water than it did in fresh water. Ships float higher in salt water, too. Civilian cargo ships, also called merchant ships, even have a mark on the side so everyone can see how high they float once their cargo is added.

This mark is called the **Plimsoll mark.** It is a safety line that shows when a ship is over-loaded. The mark is named after Samuel Plimsoll, a poor young man who managed to become elected to the British Parliament.

Even though he knew very little about the sea, he was concerned about shipwrecks that killed people. So he worked hard to make a law in Great Britain that all merchant ships be marked with a safety line.

Why was there a need for such a law? In the 1800s, sailors were required to sail on voyages no matter what—even if the ship was unsafe. Sometimes ship owners were greedy and dishonest. They would load a great deal of insured cargo onto a leaky, old ship. Then they would hope that the ship would sink when it sailed into a storm. This way, they could collect the insurance money. Many sailors lost their lives when their ships sank.

The Plimsoll safety mark prevented overloading. It showed the maximum load limit for a ship in salt water in the summer.

Later, other countries got together to establish an international load line. It has different limits for a variety of special conditions. The illustration of the ship shows the codes for these special conditions.

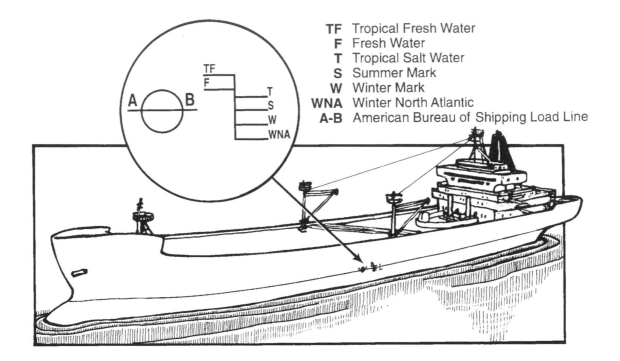

TF Tropical Fresh Water
F Fresh Water
T Tropical Salt Water
S Summer Mark
W Winter Mark
WNA Winter North Atlantic
A-B American Bureau of Shipping Load Line

Working with Mystery Cylinders

Overview and Objectives

In this final lesson, students solve a new problem by applying their knowledge about how the weight, size, and design of an object, as well as the liquid in which the object is placed, affect its buoyancy. After reflecting on the results of their investigations during the unit, students predict whether "mystery cylinders" will float or sink in fresh water and salt water and defend their predictions with specific data. Students' strategies for learning about the mystery cylinders and their reasons for their predictions will provide you with information to assess how well they have grasped the concepts and skills explored in this unit.

- Students develop a statement that generalizes how to use data to determine whether an object will float.

- Students weigh mystery cylinders with the spring scale.

- Students predict the floating behavior of mystery cylinders.

- Students test their predictions and record their results.

- Students compare the mystery cylinders to objects that they have tested in earlier lessons.

Background

This lesson is an excellent opportunity to assess what students have learned in this unit. The activities provide students with an opportunity to investigate two unknown objects—large and small "mystery cylinders"—that are made of acetyl delrin. Acetyl delrin is a type of plastic that is used to make handles for kitchen knives, among other things.

During the lesson, students weigh the large mystery cylinder with a spring scale and compare it with the other large cylinders they have investigated. They use the skills, strategies, and knowledge that they have acquired in previous lessons to predict whether the large mystery cylinder will float or sink in fresh and salt water and to give reasons for their predictions. Then they repeat the process for the small mystery cylinder.

The large mystery cylinder is the same size and shape as the other large cylinders that students have investigated, but it has a different weight, color, and texture. This gives students the opportunity to make direct comparisons between the mystery cylinder and the objects they have already worked with. The class weight graph constructed in previous lessons becomes a valuable reference tool for students in this lesson.

This lesson is an embedded assessment of students' ability to apply what they have learned about buoyancy to a new situation. Encourage students to make use of all the information they have available from previous lessons, such as graphs, charts, and drawings. Ask them to place particular emphasis on explaining the reasons for their predictions.

Materials

For each student

1 science notebook
1 copy of **Record Sheet 16-A: Making and Testing Predictions in Fresh Water**
1 copy of **Record Sheet 16-B: Making and Testing Predictions in Salt Water**
1 completed copy of **Record Sheet 12-A: The Weight of Water and Cylinders** (from Lesson 12)

For every two students

1 mystery cylinder, black, 2.5 × 2.5 cm (1 × 1″)
1 mystery cylinder, black, 1.25 × 1.25 cm (½ × ½″)
1 spring scale
1 plastic cylindrical container with masking tape handle
1 set of cylinders (from previous lessons)

For the class

2 plastic tanks, 4 liters (1 gal)
2 liters of fresh water (2 qt)
2 liters of salt water (2 qt)

Preparation

1. Make a copy of **Record Sheet 16-A: Making and Testing Predictions in Fresh Water** and **Record Sheet 16-B: Making and Testing Predictions in Salt Water** for each student.

2. Fill one tank with 2 liters of fresh water and fill the other with 2 liters of salt water from Lesson 15. Label the tanks so that students will be able to identify the two tanks of water. You may want to cover the tanks to discourage students from testing the mystery cylinders prematurely.

3. Check to be sure that the class graph prepared in previous lessons is posted in a visible location. It should include the weights of fresh water and salt water, added in Lessons 12 and 14, respectively.

Procedure

1. Ask the class to share the observations they have made and the things they have learned about floating and sinking in Lessons 1 through 15. Encourage them to review the charts, graphs, and observations they have made in previous activities. Remind them to go over the work they have done individually in their notebooks, as well as the conclusions that have been reached by the class.

2. Challenge students to write a statement in their science notebooks that generalizes how to know, before testing, whether an object will float in a liquid.

3. Show the two mystery cylinders and present the problem: Will the cylinders float or sink?

4. Challenge students to find out as much as possible about the mystery cylinders. Then distribute the mystery cylinders, spring scales, and the other cylinders that students have worked with, including the plastic cylindrical containers with masking tape handles.

Figure 16-1

*Investigating the
mystery cylinders*

5. Have students review the graphs they constructed on **Record Sheet 12-A.** Ask them to add the large and small mystery cylinders to this graph.

6. Ask students to write their predictions on **Record Sheet 16-A** and **Record Sheet 16-B.** Have them use what they learned in Step 4 to explain their reasons for each prediction.

   Note: Encourage students to elaborate on their reasons so that they are more comprehensive than simply "It's big" or "It's plastic." For example, a more complete reason might be, "I think it will sink because it's about as heavy as aluminum and aluminum sank." Even though such predictions may not match students' observations, they demonstrate that students are able to formulate testable questions. This ability represents the development of an important science skill—seeking explanations of cause-and-effect relationships.

7. Now is the time for students to test the predictions, starting with fresh water. Ask students to place the mystery cylinders one at a time into the tank marked "Fresh Water." You may want to have students test the large mystery cylinder first, followed by the small mystery cylinder. This way, all students will have a mystery cylinder to test. Remind them to record their observations on **Record Sheet 16-A.**

8. Ask students to discuss their observations and to give some possible explanations for them.

Final Activities

1. Ask students to observe what happens as they place the mystery cylinders into the tank marked "Salt Water." Remind them to record their observations and possible explanations on **Record Sheet 16-B.**

2. Discuss with students what they have observed. Ask students to share their ideas about possible explanations for their observations.

Extension

> SCIENCE

Encourage students to make predictions about whether the mystery cylinders will float or sink in other liquids. Ask them to try testing the cylinders in different kinds of shampoo or oil, for example.

Safety Tip

Some liquids that students select may be hazardous. Be sure to determine whether a particular liquid is harmful before permitting its use in the classroom.

Assessment

This lesson is designed to be an embedded assessment. It draws on experiences that students have had and the skills they have developed throughout the unit. You will see evidence of students' accomplishments on the record sheets, in their notebook entries, and in their comments and questions during class discussions.

Post-Unit Assessment

The post-unit assessment on pg. 145 is a matched follow-up to the pre-unit assessment in Lesson 1. By comparing students' pre- and post-unit responses, you will be able to document their growth in knowledge about floating and sinking.

Additional Assessments

Additional assessments for this unit are provided in Appendix A, on pg. 149. They include a self-assessment for students and assessments on applying the concepts related to floating and sinking to new situations.

Record Sheet 16-A

Name: _____

Date: _____

Making and Testing Predictions in Fresh Water

Object	My Prediction and Some Reasons	F or S	Observations and Explanations of Results
Large Mystery Cylinder			
Small Mystery Cylinder			

STC® / *Floating and Sinking*

Record Sheet 16-B

Name: _____

Date: _____

Making and Testing Predictions in Salt Water

Object	My Prediction and Some Reasons	F or S	Observations and Explanations of Results
Large Mystery Cylinder			
Small Mystery Cylinder			

STC® / *Floating and Sinking*

Post-Unit Assessment

Overview

This post-unit assessment of students' ideas about floating and sinking is matched to the pre-unit assessment in Lesson 1. By comparing the individual and class responses from Lesson 1 with the responses from these activities, you will be able to document students' learning. During the first lesson, students developed two lists—"What Do You Think Makes Objects Float or Sink?" and "What Questions Do You Have about Floating and Sinking?" They also recorded their observations of acrylic beads placed in two unidentified liquids. When students revisit these activities, they may better realize how much they have learned about floating and sinking.

Materials

For each student

    1   science notebook

    1   completed **Record Sheet 1-A: Recording Sheet** (from Lesson 1)

    1   new copy of **Record Sheet 1-A: Recording Sheet**

For the class

        Class lists from Lesson 1: "What Do You Think Makes Objects Float or Sink?" and "What Questions Do You Have about Floating and Sinking?"

    2   plastic tubes, 4.5 × 16 cm (1¾ × 6")

        Concentrated salt water

    1   acrylic bead

    1   plastic spoon

Procedure

Brainstorming Activity

1. Ask students to think about their work during the unit. What do they now know about floating and sinking? What questions do they now have? Spend five minutes writing in their notebooks what they now know about floating and sinking. Have them write their thoughts in their science notebooks. When you compare students' journal entries from Lesson 1 with their entries in this matched post-unit assessment, look for both refinement of ideas and evidence given in support of ideas.

2. Display the list "What Do you Think Makes Objects Float or Sink?" from Lesson 1. Ask students to identify statements on the list that they now

know to be true. What experiences did they have during the unit that confirmed these statements?

3. Ask students to identify statements they would like to correct or improve. What is their evidence?

4. Ask students to contribute new information to the list. What else have they learned?

5. Display the list "What Questions Do You Have about Floating and Sinking?" Ask students what questions on the list they can now answer. What new questions do they have? What are some ways to find out the answers to questions that have not yet been answered? Encourage the class to go on looking for the answers to these questions.

Acrylic Bead Experiment

1. Pour water into one of the plastic tubes until it is about two-thirds full. Fill the other tube with the same amount of saturated salt water, as you did in Lesson 1. Label the tubes "A" and "B" so that students can refer to them.

2. Place the acrylic object in each of the tubes to check whether the object will float in the salt water and sink in the fresh water. You may want to use a spoon to avoid splashing.

3. Make enough copies of **Record Sheet 1-A** for each student. Students will use the sheet as a recording sheet for the post-unit demonstration. It will be helpful if you include this sheet with students' other work products. It will give you more information about the development of students' thinking and understanding of concepts.

4. Explain to students that you are going to repeat the demonstration from Lesson 1 to find out how their ideas have changed over the past several weeks.

5. Ask students to observe what happens as you place the acrylic bead in each of the tubes. Allow several minutes for them to record their observations and ideas. Encourage them to draw pictures as well as write sentences.

6. Now ask students to look in their notebooks at the copy of Record Sheet 1-A that they completed in Lesson 1. Encourage them to compare the ideas they recorded in Lesson 1 with those recorded this time.

   Ask students to share some of the ways their ideas have changed. Questions such as the following may help students get started:

   ■ How have your ideas about this demonstration changed since Lesson 1?

   ■ What do you think are some of the reasons that your ideas have changed?

Additional Assessments

Overview

Following are some suggestions for assessment activities. Although it is not essential to do all these activities, it is recommended that students do Assessment 1.

- Assessment 1 is a self-assessment that students can use to reflect on their own learning.

- Assessment 2 invites students to describe ways to make the mystery cylinder from Lesson 16 float.

- Assessment 3 is a series of four questions about floating and sinking.

Assessment 1: Student Self-Assessment

Using a questionnaire, students assess their own learning and participation during the unit. Teachers have found it useful to meet with each student individually to discuss the self-assessment. Such meetings give you the opportunity to provide your feedback about the student's work and to compare it with the student's perceptions.

Materials

For each student

    1 **Student Self-Assessment** (blackline master on pg. 150)

Preparation

Make one copy of the **Student Self-Assessment** for each student.

Procedure

1. Discuss the **Student Self-Assessment** with the class. Explain to the students that it is important to stop from time to time and think about how they are working.

2. Allow students sufficient time to complete the self-assessment either in class or as a homework assignment.

Floating and Sinking:
Student Self-Assessment

Name: _____

Date: _____

1. What do you now know about the reasons some objects float while other objects sink that you didn't know before?

2. What do you now know about the difference between salt water and fresh water that you didn't know before?

3. How well do you think you and your partner(s) worked together? Give some examples.

4. Identify activities in the unit you enjoyed. Explain why you liked them.

5. Were there any activities in the unit you didn't understand or that confused you? Explain your answer.

6. Take another look at your record sheets, graphs, and science notebook. Describe how well you think you recorded your observations and ideas.

7. How did your work in this unit affect your attitude toward science?

Assessment 2: Making Cylinders Float

Materials

For every two students

1   black mystery cylinder, 2.5 × 2.5 cm (1 × 1″)

1   black mystery cylinder, 1.25 × 1.25 cm (½ × ½″)

Procedure

1. Invite students to think of as many ways as possible to make one of the mystery cylinders float. Ask them to write and draw their ideas in their notebooks. Encourage students to discuss their ideas with other students.

2. You may want to extend this activity by asking students to try out their ideas with actual materials.

Assessment 3: Questions about Floating and Sinking

Materials

For each student

Science notebook

1   copy of **Questions about Floating and Sinking** (blackline master on pgs. 152–154)

Preparation

Make one copy of **Questions about Floating and Sinking** for each student.

Procedure

Ask students to respond orally or in writing and drawing to questions on the blackline master, which has spaces for students' responses. Look for evidence in their responses that they have begun to make sense for themselves of the phenomena that they have experienced in the unit. You may want to encourage students to use their notebooks for this activity to help them remember what they have done in past lessons.

Questions about Floating and Sinking

Name: _____

Date: _____

1. What do you think makes some objects, such as the acrylic bead, float in salt water and sink in fresh water?

2. The tubes holding the four hydrometers shown in the picture each contain salt water. However, the saltwater solutions have different amounts of salt. Circle the hydrometer that you think is floating in the water that has the most salt. What makes you think so?

Figure A-1

Four hydrometers floating at different levels

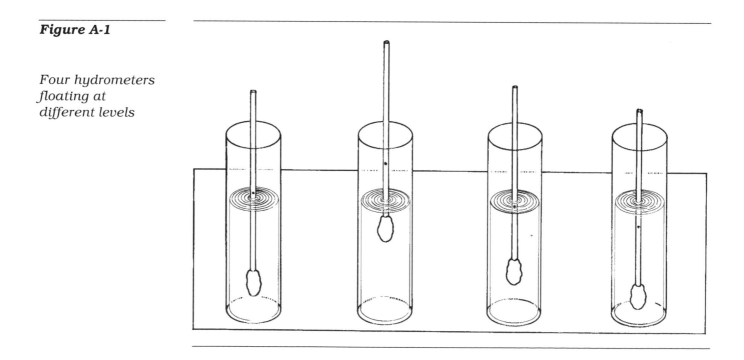

Questions about Floating and Sinking

Name: _____

Date: _____

3. Suppose that you had a lump of clay that was as big as a loaf of bread. What are at least two ways that you could make the clay float in water?

Draw pictures to help explain what you would do.

Questions about Floating and Sinking

Name: _____

Date: _____

4. The graph below shows the weight in clips of equal cupfuls of paraffin wax, ice, corn oil, and water.

Figure A-2

Demonstration graph

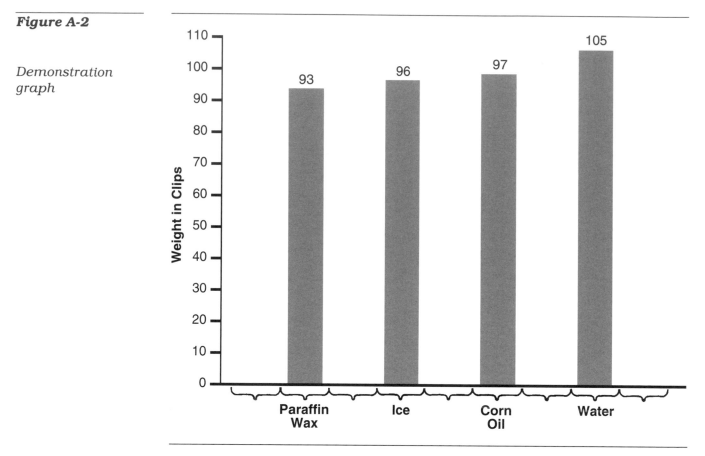

Which of the materials do you think will float in water? What makes you think so?

A cupful of salt water weighs 110 clips. Draw the salt water where you think it belongs on the graph.

Bibliography: Resources for Teachers and Books for Students

The Bibliography is divided into the following categories:

- Resources for Teachers
- Books for Students

While not a complete list of the many books written on floating and sinking, this bibliography is a sampling of books that complement this unit. These materials come well recommended. They have been favorably reviewed, and teachers have found them useful.

If a book goes out of print or if you seek additional titles, you may wish to consult the following resources.

Appraisal: Science Books for Young People (The Children's Science Book Review Committee, Boston).

> Published quarterly, this periodical reviews new science books available for young people. Each book is reviewed by a librarian and by a scientist. The Children's Science Book Review Committee is sponsored by the Science Education Department of Boston University's School of Education and the New England Roundtable of Children's Librarians.

National Science Resources Center. *Science for Children: Resources for Teachers.* Washington, DC: National Academy Press, 1988.

> This volume provides a wealth of information about resources for hands-on science programs. It describes science curriculum materials, supplementary materials (science activity books, books on teaching science, reference books, and magazines), museum programs, and elementary science curriculum projects.

Science and Children (National Science Teachers Association, Washington, DC).

> Each March, this monthly periodical provides an annotated bibliography of outstanding children's science trade books primarily for pre-kindergarten through eighth-grade science teachers.

Science Books & Films (American Association for the Advancement of Science, Washington, DC).

Published nine times a year, this periodical offers critical reviews of a wide range of new science materials, from books to audiovisual materials to electronic resources. The reviews are primarily written by scientists and science educators. *Science Books & Films* is useful for librarians, media specialists, curriculum supervisors, science teachers, and others responsible for recommending and purchasing scientific materials.

Scientific American (Scientific American, Inc., New York).

Each December, Philip and Phylis Morrison compile and review a selection of outstanding new science books for children.

Sosa, Maria, and Shirley Malcom, eds. *Science Books & Films: Best Books for Children, 1988-91*. Washington, DC: American Association for the Advancement of Science Press, 1992.

This volume, part of a continuing series, is a compilation of the most highly rated science books that have been reviewed recently in the periodical *Science Books & Films*.

Resources for Teachers

Dishon, Dee, and Pat Wilson O'Leary. *A Guidebook for Cooperative Learning: Techniques for Creating More Effective Schools*. Holmes Beach, FL: Learning Publications, 1984.

A practical guide for teachers who are embarking on the implementation of cooperative learning techniques in the classroom.

Doris, Ellen. *Doing What Scientists Do: Children Learn to Investigate Their World*. Portsmouth, NH: Heinemann Educational Books, 1991.

This comprehensive manual is filled with straightforward suggestions for bringing real science into the elementary classroom. It contains numerous examples of floating and sinking activities and is based on years of experience with elementary schoolchildren.

Johnson, David W., Roger T. Johnson, and Edythe Johnson Holubec. *Circles of Learning: Cooperation in the Classroom*. Alexandria, VA: Association for Supervision and Curriculum Development, 1984.

This excellent book presents the case for cooperative learning in a concise and readable form. It reviews the research, outlines implementation strategies, and answers many questions.

Books for Students

Clark, Eugenie. "Whale Sharks: Gentle Monsters of the Deep." *National Geographic Magazine*, December 1992, 123-39.

This article, which is accompanied by many photographs, tells the story of the author's investigation of whale sharks.

Holling, Clancy. *Paddle-to-the-Sea*. 1941. Boston: Houghton Mifflin, 1980.

This award-winning classic follows a child's model boat on its journey from a remote stream through the Great Lakes and St. Lawrence River to the Atlantic Ocean.

Humble, Richard. *Ships.* New York: Franklin Watts, 1991.

> This book is a comprehensive history of boats and ships. It is richly illustrated and well organized.

Jennings, Terry. *Floating and Sinking.* New York: Gloucester Press, 1988.

> This guide leads students through a series of interesting examples intended to demonstrate how objects float. Each demonstration is colorfully illustrated and simple to try.

Macaulay, David. *The Way Things Work.* Boston: Houghton Mifflin, 1988.

> Sections of this book deal with floating, the history of ships, and ship propulsion. The book features outstanding pictorial descriptions of various phenomena and machines.

McGovern, Ann. *Shark Lady: True Adventures of Eugenie Clark.* New York: Four Winds Press, 1978.

> A fascinating biography of an ichthyologist. The biography covers Eugenie Clark's life from her early interest in fish to her important scientific work.

Taylor, Barbara. *Sink or Swim! The Science of Water.* New York: Random House, 1991.

> A book of engaging science activities for students involving many water-related phenomena. Clear illustrations and directions make it possible for children to explore these ideas on their own.

Blackline Masters

On the following pages are large pictures of the objects that can be used to create the class graph. You can use these large pictures to make cards for Lessons 3, 5, 11, 12, and 14.

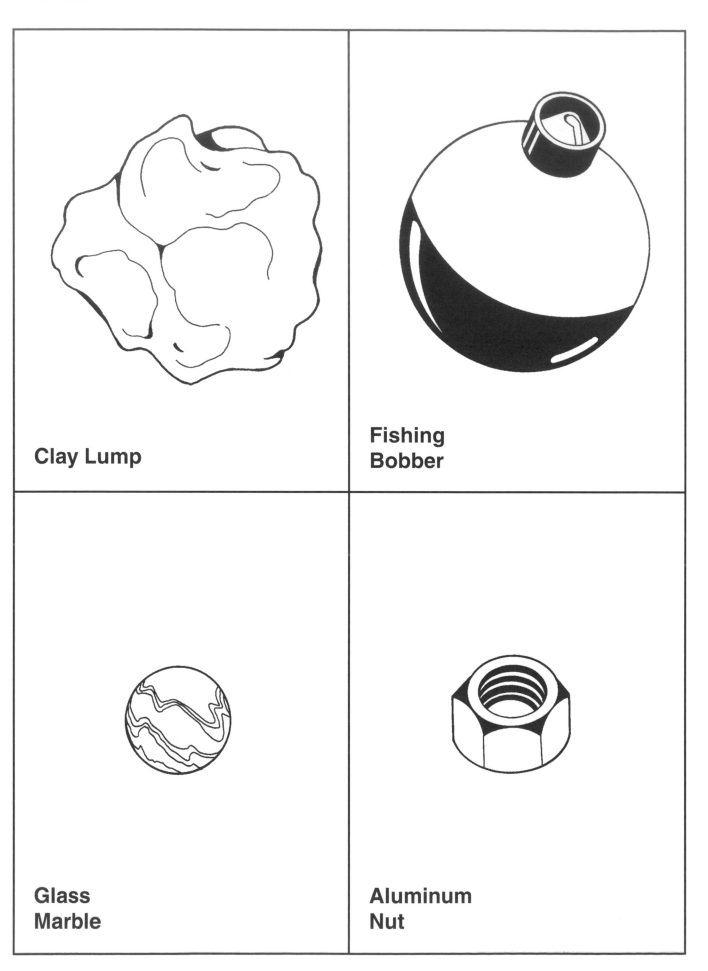

Clay Lump

**Fishing
Bobber**

**Glass
Marble**

**Aluminum
Nut**

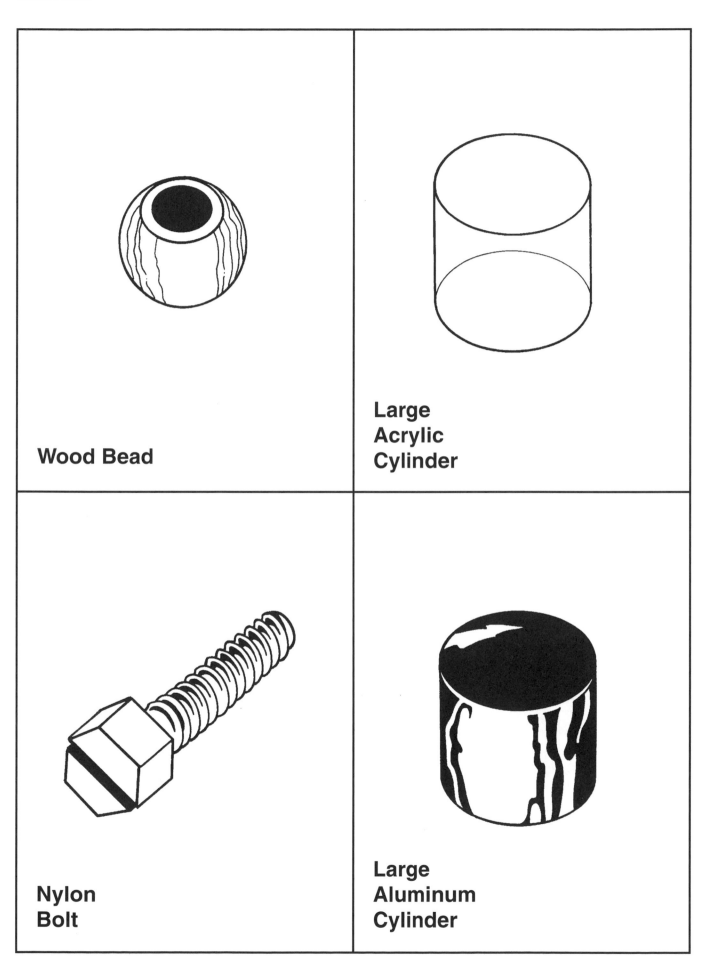

Wood Bead

**Large
Acrylic
Cylinder**

**Nylon
Bolt**

**Large
Aluminum
Cylinder**

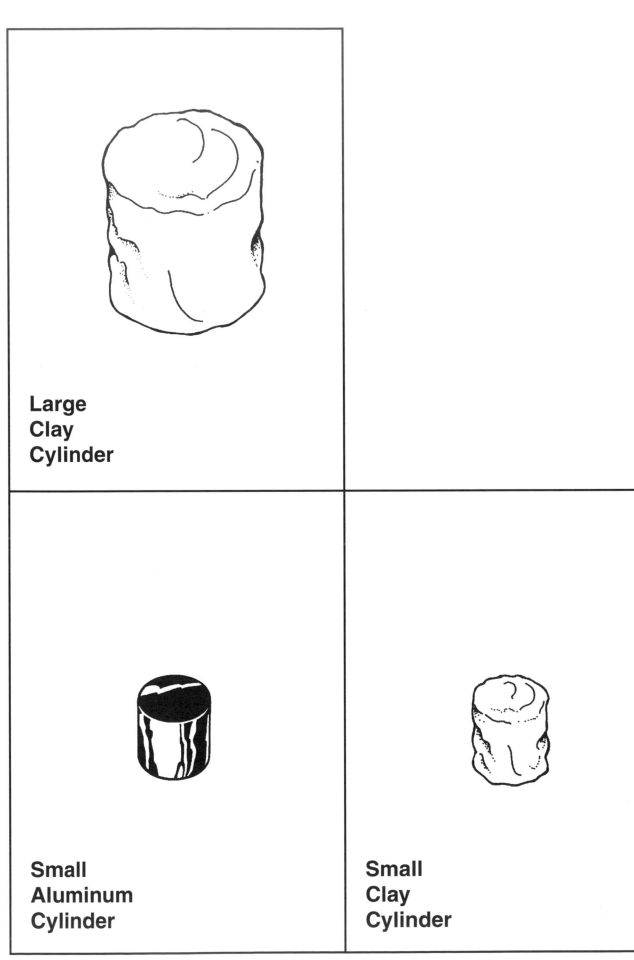

**Large
Clay
Cylinder**

**Small
Aluminum
Cylinder**

**Small
Clay
Cylinder**

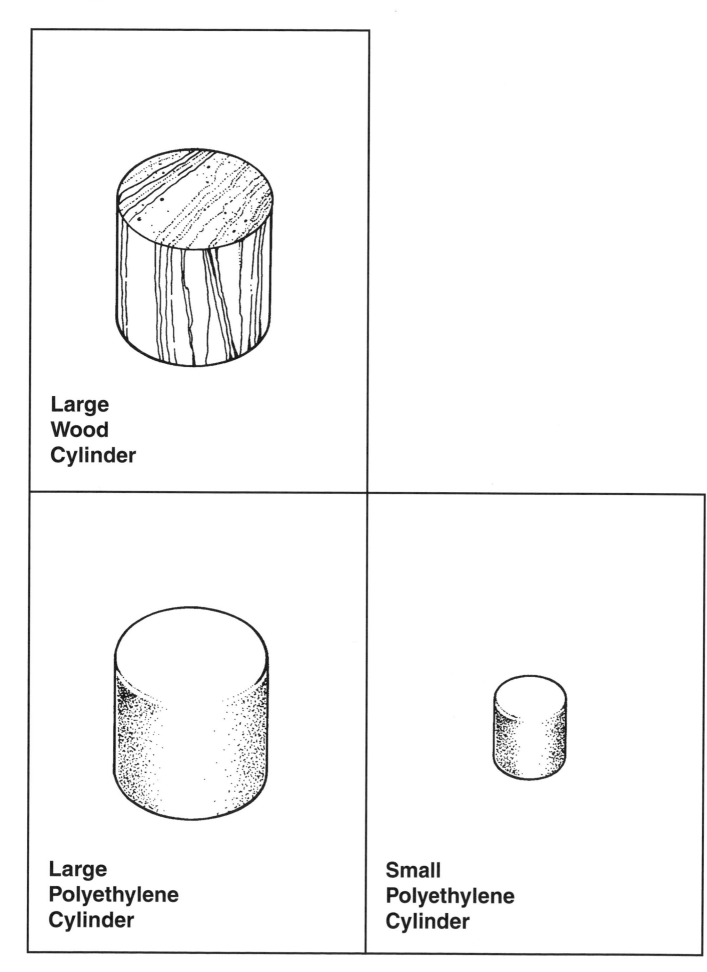

**Large
Wood
Cylinder**

**Large
Polyethylene
Cylinder**

**Small
Polyethylene
Cylinder**

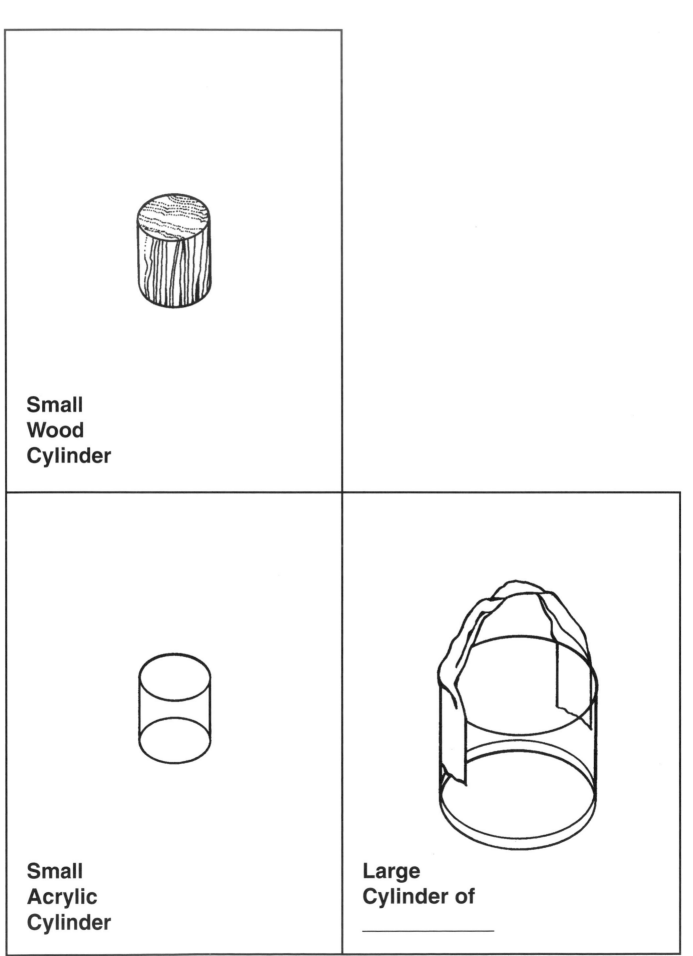

**Small
Wood
Cylinder**

**Small
Acrylic
Cylinder**

**Large
Cylinder of**

_____

How to Repair the Spring Scale

The spring scale used in this unit is designed to resist the corrosive effects of salt water while providing for the sensitive measurement of weight over as wide a range as possible. The length of the spring and tube permit both a single paper clip as well as a large aluminum cylinder to be weighed accurately. At times, however, the spring scale may need to be recalibrated or repaired. Below are a few suggestions on how to recalibrate and repair the scale.

Recalibration

When the scale needs to be recalibrated, the masking tape can be easily peeled off the plastic tube and discarded. To recalibrate the scale, attach a new piece of tape, add paper clips one at a time, and mark how far the spring stretches after each clip is added. (This procedure is described in more detail in Lesson 4.)

Figure D-1

Recalibrating the spring scale

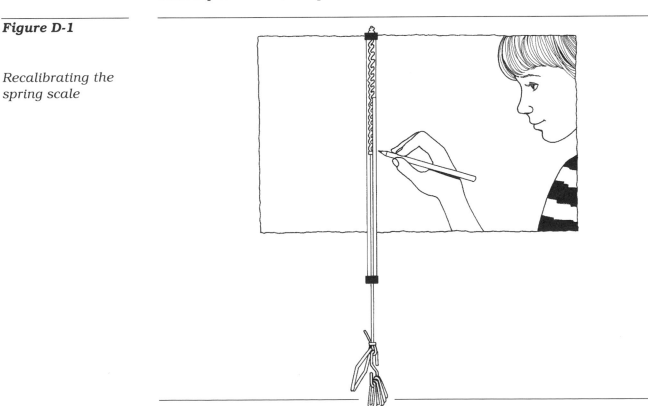

Repair

Some students may wish to remove the end caps of the scale to get a closer look at the spring. Removing the end caps is not recommended, because the spring may lose its proper shape. If the spring loses its shape, gently twist it back into a spiral and replace the end caps. It is a good idea to have students check the calibration of their scales after any repairs have been made.

Figure D-2

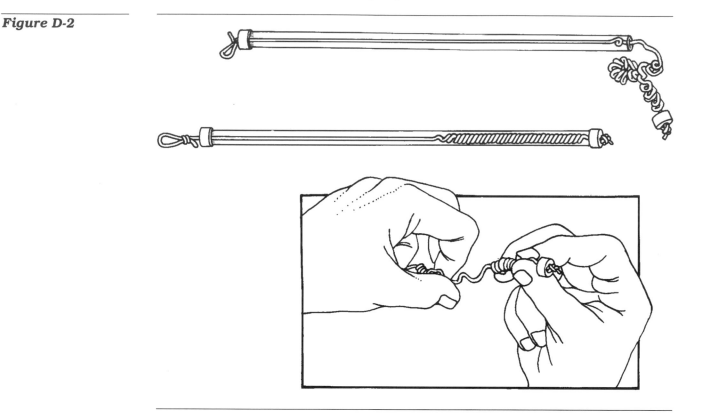

Glossary

Analyze: To study something by breaking it down into simpler parts.

Balance: An instrument for weighing (determining mass); a steady position or condition that occurs when there are two equal and opposing forces.

Buoyancy: The upward force that a fluid exerts on an object that is placed in it; the tendency of an object to float in a fluid.

Buoyant force: The pressure pushing up on an object in water or air.

Calibrate: To check, adjust, or measure exactly; to put the measuring marks on a spring scale, thermometer, or other similar device.

Classify: To group things together because they share one or more properties.

Conclusion: A decision that is based on observation or on a study of data.

Constant: A condition that is not changed in a scientific experiment.

Construct: To make by putting together parts.

Controlled experiment: A scientific investigation in which one variable is changed and all the others are kept the same, or constant.

Data: Information, such as that gathered during an experiment.

Dense: Packed closely together.

Density: The amount, or mass, of a specific volume of a substance.

Design: A sketch or model that shows how something is or is to be built.

Displacement: The process by which an object pushes aside the liquid into which it has been placed.

Dissolve: To make or become liquid.

Distribute: To spread out.

Equal: The same in amount, size, value, quality, or other characteristics.

Evidence: Something that offers proof.

Exert: To make use of; to apply.

Experiment: A procedure that is carried out to investigate a scientific question.

Float: To rest on or at the surface of, or be suspended in, a liquid.

Fluid: A substance that flows or takes the shape of its container. Both liquids and gases are fluids.

Gram (g): A unit of mass in the metric system.

Gravity: The attraction of the earth or other bodies for any object at or near their surface. The force of gravity depends on the masses of the objects and how far apart they are.

Greater: Larger in size, number, or amount.

Hydrometer: A tool used to determine the density of a liquid by comparing it with the density of water.

Hypothesis: A prediction about how something works or how two variables are related.

Invent: To think up or create something for the first time.

Liquid: A substance that has no shape but does have volume.

Mass: The amount of matter that an object contains. Mass is expressed in grams or ounces.

Mean: The number that falls an equal distance between two extremes; the average. To determine the mean, add the numbers in a set and divide the total by the number of items. For example, the mean of 1, 3, 5, 7, and 9 is 5 (25 divided by 5).

Median: The middle number in a set of numbers. If the set of numbers is 22, 33, and 44, the median is 33.

Mode: The number that occurs most often in a set of numbers. In the series 2, 4, 6, 6, 10, the mode is 6.

Pattern: A repeating arrangement of shapes, colors, numbers, or other things.

Plimsoll mark: A safety line on the outside of a cargo ship. As long as the Plimsoll mark is visible, the ship is not overloaded. If the ship begins to sink into the water because it is carrying too much cargo, the Plimsoll mark disappears.

Plot: To locate a point or points on a graph.

Procedure: A set of steps that explains how to do something.

Result: Outcome of an experiment.

Saturate: To soak or fill something until it cannot absorb or dissolve any additional material.

Saturated solution: A solution that cannot dissolve any additional material.

Sink: To move downward; to go to the bottom of.

Solid: A substance that takes up space and has its own shape.

Solution: A liquid in which something has been dissolved.

Submerge: To put under water or other liquid.

Variable: An element in an experiment that can be changed.

Volume: The amount of space that a substance takes up.

Weigh: To measure how heavy something is.

Weight: A measurement of how heavy something is.

National Science Resources Center Advisory Board

Chair
S. Anders Hedberg, Director, Science Education Initiatives, Bristol-Myers Squibb Foundation, Princeton, N.J.

Members
Gaurdie E. Banister, President, Shell Services International, Inc., Houston, Tex.

Ann Bay, Associate Director, George Washington's Mount Vernon Estate and Gardens, Mount Vernon, Va.

Goéry Delacôte, Executive Director, The Exploratorium, San Francisco, Calif.

Peter Dow, President, First-Hand Learning, Inc., Buffalo, N.Y.

Joyce Dutcher, Project Manager, Houston Urban Learning Initiative, Houston Independent School District, Houston, Tex.

Hubert M. Dyasi, Director, The Workshop Center, City College School of Education (The City University of New York), New York, N.Y.

Sylvia A. Earle, Director, Chair, and Founder, DOER Marine Operation, Oakland, Calif.

Guillermo Fernández de la Garza, Executive Director, United States-Mexico Foundation for Science, Mexico City, Mexico

Bernard S. Finn, Curator, Division of Electricity and Modern Physics, National Museum of American History, Smithsonian Institution, Washington, D.C.

Elsa Garmire, Professor, Thayer School of Engineering, Dartmouth College, Hanover, N.H.

Richard M. Gross, Vice President and Director, Research and Development, The Dow Chemical Company, Midland, Mich.

Richard Hinman, Senior Vice President for Research and Development (retired), Central Research Division, Pfizer Inc., Groton, Conn.

David Jenkins, Associate Director for Interpretive Programs, National Zoological Park, Smithsonian Institution, Washington, D.C.

John W. Layman, Professor Emeritus of Education and Physics, University of Maryland, College Park, Md.

Leon M. Lederman, Nobel Laureate, Resident Scholar, Illinois Mathematics and Science Academy, Aurora, Ill., and Director Emeritus, Fermi National Accelerator Laboratory, Batavia, Ill.

Thomas T. Liao, Professor and Chair, Department of Technology and Society, and Director, Professional Education Program, College of Engineering and Applied Sciences, State University of New York, Stony Brook, N.Y.

Theodore A. Maxwell, Associate Director, Collections and Research, National Air and Space Museum, Smithsonian Institution, Washington, D.C.

Mara Mayor, Director, The Smithsonian Associates, Smithsonian Institution, Washington, D.C.

Joseph A. Miller, Jr., Senior Vice President, Research and Development, and Chief Technology Officer, E.I. du Pont de Nemours & Company, Wilmington, Del.

John A. Moore, Professor Emeritus, Department of Biology, University of California, Riverside, Calif.

Cherry A. Murray, Director of Physical Sciences, Bell Labs, Lucent Technologies, Murray Hill, N.J.

Carlo Parravano, Director, The Merck Institute for Science Education, Rahway, N.J.

Robert W. Ridky, Professor, Department of Geology, University of Maryland, College Park, Md.

Robert D. Sullivan, Associate Director for Public Programs, National Museum of Natural History, Smithsonian Institution, Washington, D.C.

Gerald F. Wheeler, Executive Director, National Science Teachers Association, Arlington, Va.

Meredith Harris Willcuts, Science Coordinator/Science Specialist, Walla Walla School District, Walla Walla, Wash.

Paul H. Williams, Emeritus Professor, Wisconsin Fast Plants Program, University of Wisconsin, Madison, Wis.

Karen L. Worth, Senior Associate, Urban Elementary Science Project, Education Development Center, Newton, Mass.

Ex Officio Members
E. William Colglazier, Executive Officer, National Academy of Sciences, Washington, D.C.

Michael Feuer, Executive Director, Center for Science, Mathematics, and Engineering Education, National Research Council, Washington, D.C.

J. Dennis O'Connor, Under Secretary for Science, Smithsonian Institution, Washington, D.C.

Mary Tanner, Senior Executive Officer, Office of the Under Secretary for Science, Smithsonian Institution, Washington, D.C.